"If I were...
« Si j'étais...

204 Stories by Canadian Children
204 nouvelles par des jeunes Canadiens

STAPLES
Business DEPOT
www.businessdepot.com

BUREAU EN GROS
Articles de bureau • Bas prix d'entrepôt
www.bureauengros.com

It is our pleasure to donate all net proceeds
from the sale of this book to Canadian schools.

Nous sommes heureux de pouvoir faire don de toutes les recettes
nettes provenant de la vente de ce livre à des écoles canadiennes.

Published by   The Business Depot Ltd.
                   30 Centurian Drive, Suite 106
                   Markham, Ontario
                   L3R 8B9

Find us on the World Wide Web at:

businessdepot.com or at bureauengros.com

Copyright ©2002
The Business Depot Ltd.

STAPLES Business Depot/BUREAU EN GROS will donate all net proceeds from book sales for even distribution among over 200 of the Canadian schools with students submitting entries, selected by draw. Additionally, a cheque for $5,000.00 will be presented to the school of our First-Prize winner.

For further details of donations contributed to schools by
STAPLES Business Depot/BUREAU EN GROS,
please write to: P.O. Box 3619 Industrial Park Markham, ON, L3R 9Z9

Cover design: John Gale
Cover illustration: Joanne Stanbridge
First imprint: November, 2002
ISBN 0-9689688-2-1
Printed and bound in Canada

Publié par   The Business Depot Ltd.
30 Centurian Drive, Suite 106
Markham, Ontario
L3R 8B9

Nous nous trouvons sur le Web à :

bureauengros.com ou à businessdepot.com

STAPLES Business Depot/BUREAU EN GROS fera don de toutes les recettes
nettes provenant des ventes de ce livre en les distribuant équitablement entre plus
de 200 écoles des étudiants participants, choisies par tirage. De plus, un chèque de
5 000 $ sera offert à l'école du gagnant du premier prix.

Pour de plus amples détails concernant les dons faits aux écoles par
STAPLES Business Depot /BUREAU EN GROS, veuillez écrire à :
P.O. Box 3619 Industrial Park
Markham, ON, L3R 9Z9

Conception de la couverture : John Gale
Illustration de la couverture : Joanne Stanbridge
Première date de publication : Novembre 2002
ISBN 0-9689688-2-1
Imprimé et relié au Canada

Acknowledgements

STAPLES Business Depot/BUREAU EN GROS would like to thank the following organizations and individuals for their efforts in making this book possible:

- Gordon Korman, well-known Canadian children's author, for composing a story of his own and for his support of the writing project.

- COMPAQ/HP, for their generous prize donations of a computer and a digital camera.

- The Delta Group for contributions to the printing of the book.

- The thousands of children from across Canada who entered the challenge. Without their submissions we would not have been able to compile such an outstanding anthology of stories.

- All the STAPLES Business Depot/BUREAU EN GROS associates who supported this project by donating their time to serve as judges and perform administrative duties.

And... a big Thank You
to all of you who have contributed toward the education of Canadian children by purchasing this book!

Remerciements

STAPLES Business Depot/BUREAU EN GROS aimerait remercier les organisations et personnes suivantes pour les efforts fournis pour réaliser ce livre :

- Gordon Korman, célèbre auteur canadien de livres d'enfants, pour avoir composé lui-même une nouvelle et pour son aide au projet d'écriture.
- COMPAQ/HP pour leur don généreux d'un ordinateur et d'un appareil photo numérique.
- Le Delta Group pour sa contribution à l'impression de ce livre.
- Les milliers d'enfants dans tout le Canada qui ont participé au concours. Sans eux, nous ne pourrions compiler cette extraordinaire anthologie de nouvelles.
- Tous les associés de STAPLES Business Depot/BUREAU EN GROS qui ont aidé à ce projet en donnant leur temps pour servir comme juges préliminaires et effectuer les tâches administratives.

Et... un grand merci
à vous tous qui avez contribué à l'éducation des enfants canadiens en achetant ce livre !

Foreword by / **Préface par**

Steve Matyas
President/Président
STAPLES Business Depot/BUREAU EN GROS

Welcome to the second national writing challenge short story book. When we began the national writing challenge for young Canadians in 2001, we did not envision the level of support for this contest from teachers, parents and children. The comments about the difference it has made to individual children and to schools have been rewarding and most gratifying.

We want to keep making a difference to young people in Canada, by encouraging them to write creatively, to use their imaginations, and to reward them for a job well done. Who knows where creativity, imagination and literacy skills will take these young people? One only has to look as far as our guest author in this year's book, Gordon Korman, to see where a young person's writing can lead. Published at age 15, Mr. Korman has lived his dream of being an author. His books have brought enjoyment and encouraged young people to read for over two decades. All of this beginning with a grade 7 writing assignment!

The young people who submitted stories for this year's contest deserve to be congratulated. Their stories express young Canadians' dreams and values, and are a pleasure to read. I congratulate each and every one of you. Keep writing, keep imagining and keep dreaming, and who knows where it may lead you?

Thank you,

Bienvenue au second concours d'écriture de nouvelles à l'échelle nationale. Lorsqu'en 2001 nous avons lancé ce concours à l'échelle nationale pour les jeunes Canadiens, nous n'avions pas imaginé le niveau de soutien que les enseignants, les parents et les enfants donneraient à ce concours. Les commentaires concernant l'intérêt que ce concours a su créer chez les enfants et dans les écoles ont été gratifiants et flatteurs.

Nous voulons continuer à susciter l'intérêt des jeunes Canadiens en les encourageant à écrire avec créativité, à utiliser leur imagination et à les récompenser pour un travail bien fait. Qui sait où la créativité, l'imagination et les capacités de lecture et d'écriture conduiront ces jeunes ? Vous n'avez qu'à prendre l'exemple de notre auteur invité du livre de cette année, Gordon Korman, pour savoir la direction que donne l'écriture à une personne. Publié à l'âge de 15 ans, M. Korman a réalisé son rêve de devenir écrivain. Ses livres ont procuré du plaisir et, pendant plus de deux décennies, ont encouragé des jeunes à lire. Tout cela avait commencé avec une rédaction en classe de secondaire 1 !

Les jeunes, qui participent au concours de cette année en nous envoyant leurs histoires, méritent d'être félicités. Leurs histoires révèlent les rêves et les valeurs des jeunes Canadiens et procurent du plaisir à les lire. Je félicite chaque participant. Continuez à écrire, à imaginer et à rêver et qui sait où tout cela vous mènera ?

Merci.

S Matyas

Gordon Korman
Children's book author / Auteur de livres d'enfants

Dreaming is easy. And everything worth doing, or having, starts with a dream. The Olympic gold medal sprinter doesn't just take off one day and find out that he runs 100 metres faster than anyone else. First he dreams it – "If I were the world's fastest human ..." and then he strives, and trains, and makes it happen.

The challenge is to zero in on your dream, and separate the possible: "If I were Prime Minister ..." from the not-so-possible: "If I were a princess ..." and do your best to bring it about. The tools are education, training, common sense. Include yourself in the dream – your *true* self. Even a home run hitter and a medical researcher are real people. You're a real person too. What a happy coincidence! It happened for them, and it can happen for you.

So while you're dreaming "If I were ..." consider the possibility of just being you – a worthwhile person with a lot of potential to make the dream happen. And enjoy the efforts of the kids in this book, and their concise (100 words, remember?) view of what the future might hold for them.

Thank you, STAPLES Business Depot, for sponsoring their dreams.

Il est facile de rêver. Et toute chose bonne à faire ou à avoir commence avec un rêve. Ce n'est pas en se mettant à courir un jour que le coureur de vitesse qui a gagné la médaille d'or olympique découvre qu'il court les 100 mètres plus rapidement que n'importe qui d'autre. D'abord il rêve de devenir champion « Si j'étais la personne la plus rapide dans le monde... » puis il s'efforce, s'entraîne et finalement arrive à son but.

Le défi est de se concentrer sur votre rêve et de séparer le possible : « Si j'étais premier ministre ... » de l'impossible : « Si j'étais une princesse ... » et de vous efforcer le réaliser. Pour cela, les outils sont l'éducation, l'entraînement et le bon sens. Placez-vous dans votre rêve, votre vrai moi. Le joueur qui fait le coup de circuit et le chercheur médical sont des êtres humains. Vous êtes aussi un être humain. Quelle belle coïncidence ! Ça n'arrive pas qu'aux autres, ça peut vous arriver aussi.

Ainsi, lorsque vous rêvez « Si j'étais ... », pensez à la possibilité d'être seulement vous-même, une personne pleine de capacités qui peut réaliser son rêve. Et appréciez les efforts des enfants dans ce livre et la vue concise (en 100 mots seulement) de ce que l'avenir pourrait leur réserver.

Merci STAPLES Business Depot/BUREAU EN GROS de parrainer leurs rêves.

Gordon Korman was born in Montreal in 1963. At the age of seven, he moved with his family to Toronto. It was there that he wrote his first novel. In Grade 7, his Language Arts teacher gave the class four months of creative writing *carte blanche*. The result was *This Can't Be Happening At Macdonald Hall*, which was published by Scholastic in 1978.

Writing became, in rapid succession, a hobby, a summer job, and finally a full-time career. In 1985, Gordon graduated from New York University's Dramatic Writing Program. He is now the author of fifty books, including *Son Of The Mob, No More Dead Dogs, Nose Pickers From Outer Space,* and *The Monday Night Football Club* novels, which inspired the Disney TV series The Jersey.

In 2001, Gordon strayed from his trademark humour to investigate the adventure genre. The result was the *Island* trilogy, which he followed a year later with another trio, *Everest*. He has never been shipwrecked, nor does he plan to climb the world's highest mountain. Writing about these "experiences" are enough adventure for him.

Gordon lives in Long Island, New York with his wife, a Grade 4 teacher, and their two children.

Gordon Korman, New York

If I were a rock star ... if I were Prime Minister ... if I played in the NHL ... I've dreamed all these things at some point. Here's another: *If I were an author, I'd write books kids love to read.* Smaller maybe, but that dream has an advantage over the others. It came true. Millions of kids have grown up with my novels. It may be a small dream, but it's a huge feeling.

Dream big, but dream small as well. We won't all invent the wheel, but together we can make it possible to enjoy the ride.

Gordon Korman est né à Montréal en 1963. À l'âge de 7 ans, sa famille s'installe à Toronto. C'est dans cette ville qu'il écrit son premier roman. En classe de secondaire 1, son professeur de langues donne à la classe 4 mois pour écrire quelque chose de créatif dont le sujet est libre. Le résultat est *This Can't Be Happening At Macdonald Hall* qui fut publié par Scholastic en 1978.

L'écriture a été successivement son violon d'Ingres, un emploi d'été et finalement sa carrière. En 1985, Gordon a reçu son diplôme du programme d'écriture dramatique de la *New York University*. Il a écrit jusqu'à présent 50 livres dont *Son Of The Mob*, *No More Dead Dogs*, *Nose Pickers From Outer Space*, et les romans de la série *The Monday Night Football Club* qui ont inspiré le feuilleton pour la télé de Disney, *The Jersey*.

En 2001, Gordon s'est détaché de son humour de marque pour se lancer dans le genre roman d'aventure qui a donné la trilogie *Island*, laquelle a été suivie, un an plus tard, d'une autre trilogie, *Everest*. Il n'a jamais été un naufragé et ne prévoit pas être alpiniste pour grimper la montagne la plus élevée du monde. Écrire au sujet de ces « expériences » est déjà assez aventureux pour lui.

Gordon vit à Long Island, New York, avec sa femme, enseignante de classe de 4ᵉ, et leurs deux enfants.

Gordon Korman, New York

Si j'étais un chanteur rock... Si j'étais premier ministre... Si j'étais joueur de hockey dans la LNH... J'ai rêvé de tout cela à un moment donné. En voici un autre à ajouter à la liste : *Si j'étais écrivain, j'aurais écrit des livres que les enfants aimeraient lire.* Ce rêve, peut-être modeste, a pourtant un avantage sur les autres. Il s'est réalisé. Des millions d'enfants ont grandi avec mes romans. Ce rêve est peut-être modeste mais le sentiment est remarquable.

Rêvez grand sans pourtant dédaigner les rêves modestes. Nous ne pouvons pas tous inventer la roue, mais, ensemble, nous pouvons rendre le tour agréable.

First Place
Première place

Iain Bauer

Age 10, St. Albert, AB, Bertha Kennedy Catholic School

Illustrated by/Illustration par Joanne Stanbridge

If I were a skipping stone, round, smooth and flat, I would be waiting to be discovered by a child. Not too young a child that I am not thrown properly and yet not too old that I am thrown without delight. As the waves lap against me I listen to the ancient sands telling how they were ground to grains. I almost lose hope until I feel the warmth of a ten year old boy's hand against my cool surface. He holds me tightly, then throws. I dip and soar again and again. I have had the perfect skip.

Iain Bauer, age 10

Iain Bauer, Age 10, St. Albert, AB
Bertha Kennedy Catholic School

If I were a skipping stone, round, smooth and flat, I would be waiting to be discovered by a child. Not too young a child that I am not thrown properly, and yet not too old that I am thrown without delight. As the waves lap against me, I listen to the ancient sands telling how they were ground to grains. I almost lose hope until I feel the warmth of a ten year old boy's hand against my cool surface. He holds me tightly, then throws. I dip and soar again and again. I have had the perfect skip.

If I were tomorrow I'd be fresh with no mistakes. I could offer you a clean slate, new hopes, challenges and the chance to learn from the past. I could also give you the opportunity to conquer your fears, to turn foe into friend and to achieve goals that were seemingly impossible the day before. You might be afraid of me because you are afraid of the unknown. Or perhaps you are afraid I'll bring you sadness and pain. But if you think of me in a positive way, I will try to reward you with happiness.

Michelle Cannon, Age 10

Michelle Cannon, Age 10, Caledon East, ON
Herb Campbell Public School

If I were tomorrow I'd be fresh, with no mistakes. I could offer you a clean slate, new hopes, challenges, and the chance to learn from the past. I could also give you the opportunity to conquer your fears, to turn foe into friend and to achieve goals that were seemingly impossible the day before. You might be afraid of me because you are afraid of the unknown. Or perhaps you are afraid I'll bring you sadness and pain. But if you think of me in a positive way, I will try to reward you with happiness.

THIRD PLACE/TROISIÈME PLACE

Si j'étais la plume d'un auteur, je ferais jaillir mille merveilles de ma pointe effilée. Je ferais chanter les étoiles, valser les planètes. Le ciel ne serait plus qu'un immense spectacle de sons et mouvements. Pour ajouter une touche de couleur, je pigerais dans la palette du peintre des nuances de mauve et de bleu pour créer de toutes pièces une aurore boréale fabuleuse. Aussi, pour l'ambiance, je sortirais mes plus beaux synonymes et inventerais un choeur de violons éplorés secondé de quelques violoncelles lyriques. Ce serait tout un spectacle !

Sarah Boucher   13 ans

Sarah Boucher, 13 ans, Longueuil, QC
Collège Durocher St-Lambert

Si j'étais la plume d'un auteur, je ferais jaillir mille merveilles de ma pointe effilée. Je ferais chanter les étoiles, valser les planètes. Le ciel ne serait plus qu'un immense spectacle de sons et mouvements. Pour ajouter une touche de couleur, je pigerais dans la palette du peintre des nuances de mauve et de bleu pour créer de toutes pièces une aurore boréale fabuleuse. Aussi, pour l'ambiance, je sortirais mes plus beaux synonymes et inventerais un chœur de violons éplorés secondé de quelques violoncelles lyriques. Ce serait tout un spectacle!

If I were a purple flying pickle, I'd fly across the sky all the way to flying pickle land! The cucumbers would all greet me on their way to the pickling salon. As I'd fly by I'd say "Hi!" Then I'd fly to the picklemart and buy some yummy flying pickle grub. The wee sales guy at the cash register would ask if I'd pay, cash or charge. I would reply, "Neither!" and I would rush out the door 'cause Flying pickles don't have to pay. Oh, life would be perfect if I were a flying pickle! But, I am not.

Stephanie Allan, 10

Stephanie Allan, Age 10, Kingston, NS
Kingston and District School

If I were a purple flying pickle I'd fly across the sky all the way to flying pickle land! The cucumbers would all greet me on their way to the pickling salon. As I'd fly by, I'd say "Hi!" then I'd fly to the Pickle Mart and buy some yummy flying pickle grub. The wee sales guy at the cash register would ask if I'd pay cash or charge. I would reply "Neither!" and I would rush out the door 'cause flying pickles don't have to pay! Oh, life would be perfect if I were a flying pickle! But I am not.

If I were... Ogopogo I would swim all over the place. I would eat fish, seaweed sallad, rubber, metal, gas and shells. I'd live in a big cave covered in seaweed and tons of buried treasure in lake Okanogan. My best friend would be Bailey another Sea monster. Bailey and I would have fin fights and play celp ball. Bailey would have a little sister named Sidney. She can be a big pain. we also play Creature in the middle with a beach ball that would blow off the beach. I would be green with black spots and yellow spikes.

Ashlee Allbury   age: 10

Ashlee Allbury, Age 10, Lantzville, BC
Seaview School

If I were Ogopogo, I would swim all over the place. I would eat fish, seaweed, salad, rubber, metal, gas, and shells. I'd live in a big cave covered in seaweed and tons of buried treasure, in Lake Okanagan. My best friend would be Bailey, another sea monster. Bailey and I would have fin fights and play kelp ball. Bailey would have a little sister named Sidney. She can be a big pain. We also play 'creature in the middle' with a beach ball that would blow off the beach. I would be green with black spots and yellow spikes.

If I were a French/English dictionary, people would flip me over, say, "You're French!", then flip me over, say "Now You're English!" They'd get a kick out of that. Then I'd split in two and run away. The English half would go to France, say "Vive la France!", would eat some pastries and cheese. The two halves of me would rejoin. I'd go back to Canada, find a Canadian, flip him/her over and say "Ha! You're French!", flip him/her over and say "Ha! You're English!" Done.

David Andrews 13

David Andrews, Age 13, Etobicoke, ON
John English Middle School

If I were a French/English dictionary, people would flip me over, say, "You're French!", then flip me over, say "Now you're English!" They'd get a kick out of that. Then I'd split in two and run away. The English half would go to England to see the Queen. The French half would go to France, say "Vive la France!", would eat some pastries and cheese. The two halves of me would rejoin. I'd go back to Canada, find a Canadian, flip him/her over, and say "Ha! You're French!", flip him/her over, and say "Ha! You're English!" Done.

Si j'étais...

Si j'étais un ange, j'étendrais mes ailes pour m'envoler dans le firmament. Explorer l'univers, découvrir le système solaire. Sauter sur les étoiles filantes et disparaître dans une buée intense. Me retrouver sur une planète inconnue à la recherche d'un astre perdu. Solitaire, je le trouverai, pour éclairer l'humanité.

Daniel April, 11 ans

Daniel April, 11 ans, Trois-Pistoles, QC
École Litalien

Si j'étais un ange, j'étendrais mes ailes pour m'envoler dans le firmament. Explorer l'univers, découvrir le système solaire. Sauter sur les étoiles filantes et disparaître dans une buée intense. Me retrouver sur une planète inconnue à la recherche d'un astre perdu. Solitaire, je le trouverai, pour éclairer l'humanité.

If I were normal, my best friend would be human instead of my cat, Montey. If I were normal, I would have been a princess for Halloween instead of Rose, from the movie 'Titanic'. If I were normal, my favourite singers would be Britney Spears or the Backstreet Boys instead of Elvis and The Beatles. If I were normal I would beg my parents to take me to Toys"R"Us instead of Chapters. If I were normal my name would be Emily instead of Elle, but, hey, nobody's normal. Being weird is normal.

THE END

Elle Armstrong, 9

Elle Armstrong, Age 9, Dundas, ON
Central Park School

If I were normal, my best friend would be human instead of my cat, Montey. If I were normal, I would have been a princess for Halloween instead of Rose, from the movie 'Titanic'. If I were normal, my favourite singers would be Britney Spears or the Backstreet Boys instead of Elvis and The Beatles. If I were normal, I would beg my parents to take me to Toys'R'Us instead of Chapters. If I were normal my name would be Emily instead of Elle, but, hey, nobody's normal. Being weird is normal! The End.

If I were an eagle I would be flying in the sky with the wind blowing on my face. I would feel the power of my wings. I would fly free wherever I wanted to go. I would soar through the trees without letting my wings touch the branches. I would dive with my beak pointing towards the earth. My wings are tight against my sides and my feet are pointing straight behind me. Just as I get close to the ground I straighten my feet out and I try to grab my prey without it knowing I'm coming!
    Robyn Starr Arsenault age10

Robyn Starr Arsenault, Age 10, Summerside, PEI
Somerset Kinkora School

If I were an eagle, I would be flying in the sky with the wind blowing on my face. I would feel the power of my wings. I would fly free wherever I wanted to go. I would soar through the trees without letting my wings touch the branches. I would dive with my beak pointing toward the earth. My wings are tight against my sides and my feet are pointing straight behind me. Just as I get close to the ground, I straighten my feet out and I try to grab my prey without it knowing I'm coming!

Si j'étais un cheval volant, je volerai dans tous les vents. Je serai multicolore avec des sabots en or. Je donnerai de jolis rêves aux enfants endormis. J'aurai plein d'amis comme la Grande Ourse. Chaque nuit, des guerriers de Troie formés d'étoiles me brosseront les poils, la crinière, ma queue et feront briller mes beaux sabots. Parfois, les enfants rêvent de moi, le cheval volant.

Bouchra Assabah, 10 ans.

Bouchra Assabah, 10 ans, Laval, QC
École Abi Talib

Si j'étais un cheval volant, je volerai dans tous les vents. Je serais multicolore, avec des sabots en or. Je donnerais de jolis rêves aux enfants endormis. J'aurais plein d'amis comme la Grande Ourse. Chaque nuit, des guerriers de Troie formés d'étoiles me brosseront les poils, la crinière, ma queue, et feront briller mes beaux sabots. Parfois, les enfants rêvent de moi, le cheval volant.

If I were to write, A book about our world,
About our loves and laughs, The troubles we unfurled,

For thousands of years, We waited and stood,
Alone in our time, Then we let down our hood,

For those who have followed, And those who soon will,
We give you our thoughts, The soil you shall till,

Some say we have left, Much turmoil and guilt,
A home like a flower, Almost ready to wilt,

But doesn't that make, Their lives all the sweeter,
A new chance to try, To show the Creator,

How we can grow, And also achieve. ★

Julia Attwood, 12

Julia Attwood, Age 12, Dartmouth, NS
Shambhala School

If I were to write a book about our world, about our loves and laughs,
the trouble we unfurled. For thousands of years, we waited and stood,
alone in our time, then we let down our hood. For those who have
followed, and those who soon will, we give you our thoughts, the soil
you shall till. Some say we have left much turmoil and guilt, a home
like a flower, almost ready to wilt. But doesn't that make their lives
all the sweeter? A new chance to try, to show the Creator. How we can
grow, and also achieve.

If I were a survivor of the September terrorist attacks on the Twin Towers, I hope I would be able to say that I did everything in my power to help others escape before these massive buildings collapsed. I would write about my experience and tell others about the importance of loving and respecting each other regardless of culture, religion, political views, colour, or race. My story would be dedicated to the victims and their families. However, if I died that day I would expect others to comfort my family and do their best to prevent future violence by terrorist.

Jared, age 13, Ontario

Jared Ayton, Age 13, Sault Ste. Marie, ON
Tarentorus Public School

If I were a survivor of the September terrorist attacks on the twin towers, I hope I would be able to say that I did everything in my power to help others escape before these massive buildings collapsed. I would write about my experience and tell others about the importance of loving and respecting each other, regardless of culture, religion, political views, colour, or race. My story would be dedicated to the victims and their families. However, if I died that day, I would expect others to comfort my family, and do their best to prevent future violence by terrorists.

If I were a hippo I'd be Called Linda. I would have a whole bunch of hip hippo friends. We would find a tree, jump off and do bellyflops. We would swim and soak in our mudbaths the whole day. One day when busy swimming a hunter came by and saw us practising for the belly flop championship. A GUN! It was scary! We started doing synchronized swimming. "Nope, wrong choice!" Now, we are not ordinary hippos. We dove underwater and zoomed up into the air. He ran away scared and never came back

The End

Lindsay Bailey Age 10

Lindsay Bailey, Age 10, Crofton, BC
Crofton Elementary School

If I were a hippo, I'd be called Linda. I would have a whole bunch of hip hippo friends. We would find a tree, jump off, and do belly flops. We would swim and soak in our mudbaths the whole day. One day, when busy swimming, a hunter came by and saw us practising for the belly flop championship. A gun! It was scary! We started doing synchronized swimming. "Nope, wrong choice." Now, we are not ordinary hippos. We dove underwater and zoomed up into the air. He ran away scared and never came back. The end.

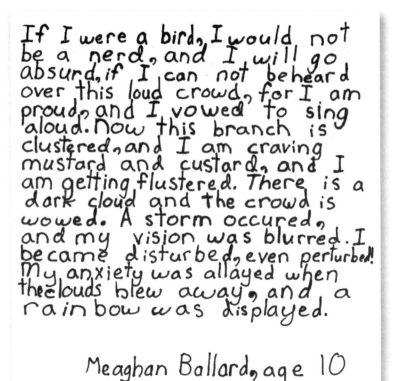

If I were a bird, I would not be a nerd, and I will go absurd, if I can not be heard over this loud crowd, for I am proud, and I vowed to sing aloud. Now this branch is clustered, and I am craving mustard and custard, and I am getting flustered. There is a dark cloud and the crowd is wowed. A storm occured, and my vision was blurred. I became disturbed, even perturbed! My anxiety was allayed when the clouds blew away, and a rainbow was displayed.

Meaghan Ballard, age 10

Meaghan Ballard, Age 10, Winnipeg, MB
Pacific Junction School

If I were a bird, I would not be a nerd, and I will go absurd, if I cannot be heard over this loud crowd, for I am proud, and I vowed to sing aloud. Now this branch is clustered, and I am craving mustard and custard, and I am getting flustered. There is a dark cloud and the crowd is wowed. A storm occurred, and my vision was blurred. I became disturbed, even perturbed! My anxiety was allayed when the clouds blew away, and a rainbow was displayed.

Si j'étais reine de ce monde, j'imposerais une loi.
Que tous les couples désirant avoir plus d'un enfants doivent pour le deuxième faire la demande pour une adoption. Je trouve qu'il y a trop d'enfants qui n'ont pas de famille, et c'est très injuste. Aussi je pense que ce serait mieux pour notre monde, il y aurait moin de pauvreté et les gens pourrais apprendre a vivre avec d'autres cultures. Ce serais un monde meilleur, et peut être même moin de querre. Adopter un enfant c'est etre conscient de notre planete un peu comme recycler.

Eva-Ana Barroso Riccardi, 9ans.

Eva-Ana Barroso Riccardi, 9 ans, Montréal, QC
École Nesbitt

Si j'étais reine de ce monde, j'imposerais une loi. Que tous les couples désirant avoir plus d'un enfant doivent, pour le deuxième, faire la demande pour une adoption. Je trouve qu'il y a trop d'enfants qui n'ont pas de famille et c'est très injuste. Aussi je pense que ce serait mieux pour notre monde, il y aurait moins de pauvreté et les gens pourraient apprendre à vivre avec d'autres cultures. Ce serait un monde meilleur, et peut-être même moins de guerre. Adopter un enfant, c'est être conscient de notre planète, un peu comme recycler.

Gabbi Bernard, Age 10, Sherwood Park, AB
Woodbridge Farms School

If I were in a world of nothingness, a place where nothing existed, and I was nothing myself, what would life be like? To question the matter more, would there be life at all? No body, no mind, not even a soul? Nothing, no people to see, no songs to hear? Not existing at all, yet still some small morsel exists, but no one, not even you, knows. People often take life as if it was the only way to be. Well, ask yourself: What if you hadn't been granted the experience of life? Imagining the unimaginable, questioning the unanswerable.

If I were the earth, a sublime, majestic sphere, I would eagerly continue my billion-year-old journey, gracefully orbiting around the sun, for milleniums to come. Never forgetting to pay visits to each and every constellation, reaching the brink of the universe, unmistakably, would be no option. As I would spin endlessly as an impeding carousel, I would repeat to my fellow human friends the saying that for so many years I have been trying to tell: "Take care of me for I have given you a home. Treat me kindly for one day I shall be gone."

Mélanie Bernier 13½ yrs.

Mélanie Bernier, Age 13, Welland, ON
Sacré-Coeur School

If I were the Earth, a sublime, majestic sphere, I would eagerly continue my billion-year-old journey, gracefully orbiting around the sun, for millenniums to come. Never forgetting to pay visits to each and every constellation. Reaching the brink of the universe, unmistakably, would be no option, as I would spin endlessly like an impeding carousel.
I would repeat to my fellow human friends the saying that for so many years I have been trying to tell: "Take care of me for I have given you a home. Treat me kindly, for one day I shall be gone."

If I were a police officer I could fight crime and save lives. If I were a musician I could make music and touch people's hearts. If I were a scientist I could use a microscope and make discoveries. I could help find a cure for cancer or AIDS. If I were a parent I could give a child love. But if I were a teacher I could teach kids like me that they can do anything. Some day they could be police officers, musicians, scientists or parents. Then all things become possible.

Emily Berntson, 12

Emily Berntson, Age 12, Saskatoon, SK
Caswell School

If I were a police officer I could fight crime and save lives. If I were a musician, I could make music and touch people's hearts. If I were a scientist, I could use a microscope and make discoveries. I could help find a cure for cancer and AIDS. If I were a parent, I could give a child love. But if I were a teacher, I could teach kids like me that they can do anything. Someday, they could be police officers, musicians, scientists or parents. Then all things become possible.

If I were a horse, I would trot gallantly away from my barn and gather up my powerful limbs to leap magnificently over the fence; my muscular legs curled up underneath me. I would gallop across lush springy grass, relishing the feeling of freedom and delight that surround me; turbulence and strength working together like rushing water. Then, I would curl up in ecstasy among fluorescent flowers, their vivid fragrance enveloping my beautiful face. Under the cool evening stars, I would canter back to my homely stall and sweet smelling hay, deep satisfaction reflecting in my large ebony eyes.

Claire Bibby, 12

Claire Bibby, Age 12, Princeton, BC
Riverside Intermediate School

If I were a horse, I would trot gallantly away from my barn and gather up my powerful limbs to leap magnificently, over the fence, my muscular legs curled up underneath me. I would gallop across lush, springy green grass, relishing the feeling of freedom and delight that surrounds me; turbulence and strength working together like rushing water. Then, I would curl up in ecstasy among fluorescent flowers, their vivid fragrance enveloping my beautiful face. Under the cool evening stars, I would canter back to my homey stall and sweet-smelling hay, deep satisfaction reflecting in my large, ebony eyes.

Si j'étais ingénieur, je ferais un projet que je veux faire depuis que je suis petit. Mon projet se nomme Jet-Moto. Je veux inventer une moto qui vole. Elle aura deux ailes sur le côté et un réacteur avant. Elle ira plus vite qu'une moto de course et elle ne pollura pas. Non, au contraire, mon jet filtrera le CO_2 et le transformera en oxygène pur. Peut-être que les usines feront du CO_2 mais le même mécanisme sera appliqué sur les usines. Il faudra que je me spécialise dans les mathématiques. Je suis déjà très bon en mathématique.

Jocelyn Bisson, 10 ans

Jocelyn Bisson, 10 ans, St-Constant, QC
École Jacques Barclay

Si j'étais ingénieur, je ferais un projet que je veux faire depuis que je suis petit. Mon projet se nomme Jet-Moto. Je veux inventer une moto qui vole. Elle aura deux ailes sur le côté et un réacteur avant. Elle ira plus vite qu'une moto de course et elle ne polluera pas. Non, au contraire, mon jet filtrera le CO2 et le transformera en oxygène pur. Peut-être que les usines feront du CO2 mais le même mécanisme sera appliqué sur les usines. Il faudra que je me spécialise dans les mathématiques. Je suis déjà très bon en mathématiques.

If I were four inches tall for a day, I would be too small to get out of bed. A cheerio would be enough to eat for breakfast. I would get buried under my clothes. My school books would be way too big for me and no one would hear me if I tried to answer a question in class. At recess I might get trampled! When I was going home on the bus I would have to hold on tight. For supper I would have a french fry. At bedtime I would think about my small tough day.

Ashley Bland   Age 10

Ashley Bland, Age 10, Saint John, NB
Simonds Middle School

If I were four inches tall for a day, I would be too small to get out of bed. A cheerio would be enough to eat for breakfast. I would get buried under my clothes. My school books would be way too big for me, and no one would hear me if I tried to answer a question in class. At recess, I might get trampled! When I was going home on the bus, I would have to hold on tight. For supper, I would have a french fry. At bed time, I would think about my small, tough day.

If I were a sunflower I would raise my golden head, to catch the the warm breeze that blew by. I'd follow the sun all day long. While listening to children singing a magical song, running barefoot through the sprinkler on the freshly mowed lawn. Soon the crinkly leaves will float to the ground. Then I know that Autumn is drawing near. I will hold my heavy head and bow. The morning dew will wet my head and bring a tear across my tanned face. Soon the northeast wind will howl telling me that Jack Frost has come once again.

Melissa Boeve   9   years old

Melissa Boeve, Age 9, Abbotsford, BC
John Calvin School

If I were a sunflower, I would raise my golden head, to catch the warm breeze that blew by. I'd follow the sun all day long. While listening to children singing a magical song, running barefoot through the sprinkler on the freshly mowed lawn. Soon the crinkly leaves will float to the ground. Then I know that autumn is drawing near. I will hold my heavy head and bow. The morning dew will wet my head and bring a tear across my tanned face. Soon the northeast wind will howl, telling me that Jack Frost has come once again.

Si j'étais dans un monde fait en chocolat, je serais au paradis. Toutes les maisons seraient en chocolat blanc, et les portes en chocolat noir. Ce serait un petit monde où on ne verrait jamais l'été. On ferait du ski sur les montagnes de crème glacée et nous nagerions dans des lacs de chocolat chaud. Les villageois seraient des bonshommes de neige mais ils seraient faits en guimauves. Leur nez serait des jujubes et leurs bras, de la canelle. À la fin de la journée je mangerais tout même les villageois. Si j'étais dans ce monde je pèserais trois cents livres!

Emily Bradley 12 ans

Emily Bradley, 12 ans, Aylmer, QC
Collège St-Joseph

Si j'étais dans un monde fait en chocolat, je serais au paradis. Toutes les maisons seraient en chocolat blanc et les portes en chocolat noir. Ce serait un petit monde où on ne verrait jamais l'été. On ferait du ski sur les montagnes de crème glacée et nous nagerions dans des lacs de chocolat chaud. Les villageois seraient des bonshommes de neige mais ils seraient faits en guimauves. Leur nez serait des jujubes et leurs bras de la cannelle. À la fin de la journée, je mangerais tout, même les villageois. Si j'étais dans ce monde, je pèserais trois cents livres!

If I were a flea on top of a poodle, I might scurry through curls and more curls, untill finally I would find some breakfast. After snacking on my food I might swing through curls, hoping to soon reach the other side of the dog. While swinging through more curls, and finally coming to an open space on top of the head, I might scope out all that lays before me. After peering around for a while I might slide down the pink fluffy ear and rest untill morning, and the next day I would do it all over again!

Stacey Brandsma, 12

Stacey Brandsma, Age 12, Red Deer, AB
Red Deer Christian Alternative Program

If I were a flea on top of a poodle, I might scurry through curls and more curls, until finally, I would find some breakfast. After snacking on my food, I might swing through curls, hoping to soon reach the other side of the dog. While swinging through more curls, and finally coming to an open space on top of the head, I might scope out all that lays before me. After peering around for a while, I might slide down the pink fluffy ear and rest until morning. And the next day, I would do it all over again.

If I were the wind, I would bring
cool brisk air to a hot summer day. A
child would be having fun because I
lifted his or her kite into the air. The
mighty oaks would sway in my presence.
I would help a paraglider at his/her task
at hand. At one time I could be a peaceful
winter breeze but at another, a raging hurricane.
I would blow a sheet of fog into the battle
of Afganistan, to give the brave soldiers,
against terrorism, the cover they need, to win
the war.   If I were the wind.

Jonathan Brewer   Age-13

**Jonathan Brewer, Age 13, North Vancouver, BC
Sutherland Secondary School**

If I were the wind, I would bring cool, brisk air to a hot summer day.
A child would be having fun because I lifted his or her kite into the air.
The mighty oaks would sway in my presence. I would help a paraglider
at his/her task at hand. At one time, I could be a peaceful winter breeze,
but at another, a raging hurricane. I would blow in a sheet of fog to the
battle of Afghanistan to give the brave soldiers against terrorism the
cover they need to win the war. If I were the wind.

If I were a dragon, I would breathe fire and fly high in the air. I would chase humans and destroy buildings! I would be fifty feet tall! I would have black scales and beady red eyes. I would live in a cave and eat humans and drink their flesh. My cave would be full of blood and bones; it will be dark and gloomy. It would be very deep under ground and it will be hidden on the east side of mount Everest. I will live for thousands of years.

Jordan Broomfield, 10

Jordan Broomfield, Age 10, Makkovik, Labrador, NF
John Christian Erhardt Memorial School

If I were a dragon, I would breathe fire and fly high in the air. I would chase humans and destroy buildings! I would be fifty feet tall! I would have black scales and beady red eyes! I would live in a cave and eat humans and drink their flesh! My cave would be full of blood and bones! It will be dark and very gloomy! It would be very deep underground and it will be hidden on the east side of Mount Everest. I will live for thousands of years.

Si j'étais une étoile, j'illuminerais le monde entier. Je rendrais le monde heureux en donnant de la lumière à ceux qui se sentent seuls la nuit. Avec mes soeurs les étoiles et ma mère la lune, je servirais de toile de fond aux amoureux sur un banc de parc. Les soirs de percéïdes, je m'amuserais à filer dans le ciel tout en faisant naître des voeux. Avec la nuit, je m'éteindrais fatiguée mais contente d'avoir réalisé des rêve. Pendant la journée, je rechargerais mes piles et je rêverais à tous ces gens dont j'ai illuminé la nuit.

Quel beau travail!

Alexe Brousseau 11 ans

**Alexe Brousseau, 11 ans, Ville Ste-Marie, QC
École Monseigneur Feuiltault**

Si j'étais une étoile, j'illuminerais le monde entier. Je rendrais le monde heureux en donnant de la lumière à ceux qui se sentent seuls la nuit. Avec mes sœurs les étoiles et ma mère la lune, je servirais de toile de fond aux amoureux sur un banc de parc. Les soirs de percéïdes, je m'amuserais à filer dans le ciel tout en faisant naître des vœux. Avec la nuit, je m'éteindrais fatiguée mais contente d'avoir réalisé des rêves. Pendant la journée, je rechargerais mes piles et je rêverais à tous ces gens dont j'ai illuminé la nuit. Quel beau travail!

If I were biking with Katya, we would sing our favorite song, "Going to a fairy world." "Look Jocelyn!" Katya yelled. Bluish bubbles had formed around her! Without realizing, I grasped Katya's hand! We vanished. We re-appeared in an underground cave. Groping along the wall, we saw a dim light. We heard terrible laughter. Fairies dressed in black with greenish glowing skin guarded an amulet. We knew we had to get the amulet. A fairy caught us. "The amulet of mischief breaks up friends. Take it to your world to become a regular bracelet charm," she whispered. We did it!

Jocelyn Bruce, 9

Jocelyn Bruce, Age 9, Seven Sisters, MB
Whitemouth School

If I were biking with Katya, we would sing our favourite song, "Going to a fairy's world." "Look Jocelyn!" Katya yelled. Bluish bubbles have formed around her! Without realizing, I grasped Katya's hand! We vanished! We reappeared in an underground cave. Groping along the wall we saw a dim light. We heard terrible laughter. Fairies dressed in black with greenish, glowing skin guarded an amulet. We knew we had to get the amulet! A fairy caught us. "The amulet of mischief breaks up friends. Take it to your world to become a regular bracelet charm," she whispered. We did it!

If I were water, I would fall down from the sky into clear mountain pools. I would rush fizzle, bubble into river rapids. I'd cascade in a mighty white roar over breathtaking waterfalls. I would flow past glorious scenery on the banks of rivers, carrying fishermen and kayakers downstream. I would inspire artists, authors and composers. I would play an important role in many stories. Finally, after all my adventures, I would reach the ocean, evaporate, and start the cycle all over again. If I were water, I would do extraordinary things.

Stuart Bulmer age:13

Stuart Bulmer, Age 13, Milverton, ON
Milverton Public School

If I were water, I would fall down from the sky into clear mountain pools. I would rush, fizzle, bubble into river rapids. I'd cascade in a mighty white roar over breathtaking waterfalls. I would flow past glorious scenery on the banks of rivers, carrying fishermen and kayakers downstream. I would inspire artists, authors, and composers. I would play an important role in many stories. Finally, after all my adventures, I would reach the ocean, evaporate, and start the cycle all over again. If I were water, I would do extraordinary things.

If I were a Sorceress, I would conjure the most powerful magic of the elements and create beautiful creatures to roam the Earth. They would travel far and wide, teaching mankind to appreciate what we have, not taking for granted our family, friends, and home. They would teach how to give a little, take a little, and leave some for the rest. They would teach how to replace hatred with perfect love, walk with others in blissful harmony. Then, there would be no more war or poverty. The world would be a perfect place for all.

Laura Cadrain, 12

Laura Cadrain, Age 12, Edmonton, AB
Lendrum Elementary School

If I were a sorceress, I would conjure the most powerful magic of the elements and create beautiful creatures to roam the earth. They would travel far and wide, teaching mankind to appreciate what we have, not taking for granted our family, friends and home. They would teach how to give a little, take a little, and leave some for the rest. They would teach how to replace hatred with perfect love, walk with others in blissful harmony. Then there would be no more war or poverty. The world would be a perfect place for all.

If I were a doctor I
would like to help babies
get born. I would take
care of mothers while their
babies grow inside their tummies
just like when my baby brother
Jacob grew inside my mommy's
tummy. I would measure the
mother's stomach and listen to the
baby's heartbeat. I would help the
Mom to be healthy. When it
is time for the baby to come
out I will help the baby come
out into the world and meet
it's Daddy!

Regina Canale 6 years old

Regina Canale, Age 6, Fort Langley, BC
Traditional Learning Academy

If I were a doctor, I would like to help babies get born. I would take
care of mothers while their babies grow inside their tummies, just
like when my baby brother Jacob grew inside my mommy's tummy.
I would measure the mother's stomach and listen to the baby's
heartbeat. I would help the mom to be healthy. When it is time for the
baby to come out, I will help the baby come out into the world and meet
it's daddy!

43

If I were a book, I'd let you see my words and my pages one, two, and three. I'd be full of monsters, dragons and trolls, and shining knights ever so bold. Your mind would be off in wonderous places, whether it was the ocean, the jungle, or wide open spaces. You'd be caught by my words and images too. I'd paint pictures just for you. I'd provide you with hours of adventurous tales and when it comes time to say your prayers, I'll sit while you dream of things that you've read, in you carriage of tales... your bed!

Chelsea Carey, 11

Chelsea Carey, Age 11, Calgary, AB
Dalhousie Elementary School

If I were a book, I'd let you see my words and my pages one, two, and three. I'd be full of monsters, dragons and trolls, and shining knights, ever so bold. Your mind would be off in wondrous places, whether it was the ocean, the jungle, or wide open spaces. You'd be caught by my words and images too. I'd paint pictures just for you. I'd provide you with hours of adventurous tales, and when it comes time to say your prayers, I'll sit while you dream of things that you've read, in your carriage of tales ... your bed!

If I were a Martian, I would send important messages like this one, to all human beings: This is a message direct from outer space. I might be a Martian, but I realize there is a major problem in the way humans are functioning and that something needs to be done. While some have cupboards full of food, others are starving. While some children are at school, others are working to survive. Also, the planet's health is in danger because of the pollution. If all humans would work together towards the solutions, many problems could be solved. Good luck Earthlings!

Gabrielle Carrier, 12

Gabrielle Carrier, Age 12, Cornwall, ON
L'Héritage School

If I were a martian, I would send important messages, like this one, to all human beings: This is a message direct from outer space. I might be a martian, but I realize there is a major problem in the way humans are functioning, and that something needs to be done. While some have cupboards full of food, others are starving. While some children are at school, others are working to survive. Also, the planet's health is in danger because of the pollution. If all humans would work together toward the solutions, many problems could be solved. Good luck, Earthlings!

45

Si j'étais un extra-terrestre, j'aurais trois yeux, un nez et deux bouches. Un liquide vert, visqueux et collant recouvrirait mon corps. Je visiterais toutes les planètes du système solaire. Je me promènerais en soucoupe volante et filerais dans le ciel comme une fusée interplanétaire. J'essaierais de communiquer avec les habitants des autres planètes afin de me faire des amis et d'échanger mes connaissances avec les leurs pour que nous puissions construire un univers meilleur. J'inviterais tous les enfants du monde à venir sur ma planète faire une grande fête d'amitié autour d'un feu de joie.

Fin.

Alexandra Carrière, 10 ans

Alexandra Carrière, 10 ans, Beauport, QC
École Ste-Chrétienne

Si j'étais un extraterrestre, j'aurais trois yeux, un nez, et deux bouches. Un liquide vert, visqueux et collant recouvrirait mon corps. Je visiterais toutes les planètes du système solaire. Je me promènerais en soucoupe volante et filerais dans le ciel comme une fusée interplanétaire. J'essaierais de communiquer avec les habitants des autres planètes afin de me faire des amis et d'échanger mes connaissances avec les leurs pour que nous puissions construire un univers meilleur. J'inviterais tous les enfants du monde à venir sur ma planète faire une grande fête d'amitié autour d'un feu de joie. Fin.

If I were a falcon I would soar through the air, super fast, catching birds along the way. Spinning and diving all day long, I'd dodge the poachers in the fall. I would look down below and see the world spread out before me. I would work twice as hard when I had chicks to feed, catching pigeons, gulls and more. A proud papa I would be, teaching them everything they need to know. I'd be a Peregrine falcon, doing all the things that I have mentioned. One small problem. I'm afraid of heights!

Tyler James Case age 8.

Tyler James Case, Age 8, Hamilton, ON
St. Columba School

If I were a falcon, I would soar through the air, super fast, catching birds along the way. Spinning and diving all day long, I'd dodge the poachers in the fall. I would look down below and see the world spread out before me. I would work twice as hard when I had chicks to feed, catching pigeons, gulls and more. A proud papa I would be, teaching them everything they need to know. I'd be a Peregrine falcon, doing all the things that I have mentioned. One small problem. I'm afraid of heights!

If I were rich I'd spend my money on food and I'd donate the food to the food bank. I'd also give my money to charities and buy blankets and clothing for the homeless. I'd donate money to cancer research so they could find different ways to stop the cancer. I'd give my money to schools in Canada so they could buy new equipment. I'd give money to hospitals so they could buy all the latest equipment they needed to treat their patients. If people wanted to borrow my money I'd tell them "Keep it, don't pay me back."

Bethany Chan   Age 10

Bethany Chan, Age 10, Richmond, BC
Diefenbaker School

If I were rich I'd spend my money on food and I'd donate the food to the food bank. I'd also give my money to charities and buy blankets and clothing for the homeless. I'd donate money to cancer research so they could find different ways to stop the cancer. I'd give my money to schools in Canada so they could buy new equipment. I'd give the money to hospitals so they could buy all the latest equipment they needed to treat their patients. If people wanted to borrow my money, I would tell them, "Keep it, don't pay me back."

If I were a song, I would be a song that makes everyone feel like they were lying on the clouds, having the sweetest dreams. But I would not be a song that is only for entertainment; I would be a song that can touch the hearts of those who hear me. I would help people forget their sorrows and motivate them to chase their dreams. I would take away the sadness and hatred in everyone's hearts and fill them with joy and love. I would be a song that helps to make the world a better place to live.

Irene Chen, 11

Irene Chen, Age 11, Scarborough, ON
Ellesmere-Statton Public School

If I were a song, I would be a song that makes everyone feel like they were lying on the clouds, having the sweetest dreams. But I would not be a song that is only for entertainment; I would be a song that can touch the hearts of those who hear me. I would help people forget their sorrows and motivate them to chase their dreams. I would take away the sadness and hatred in everyone's hearts and fill them with joy and love. I would be a song that helps to make the world a better place to live.

If I were a flower. What would I know how humans feel or what they do? I only dream to be human. You might think your life is unfair, but living as a flower is unfair. Will I ever experience love? No. As I stand in the cold wind, predicting when I will perish, I tell myself, I have a life, but I don't have a chance to do what I wish. I look at my reflection, I'm just a pretty flower! Unable to walk, speak, touch, hear, see, taste, love, or live my only dream. Am I truly living?

Susan Chiu — 13

Susan Chiu, Age 13, St-Laurent, QC
Villa Maria School

If I were a flower. What would I know how humans feel or what they do? I only dream to be human. You might think your life is unfair, but living as a flower is unfair. Will I ever experience love? No. As I stand in the cold wind, predicting when I will perish, I tell myself, I have a life, but I don't have a chance to do what I wish. I look at my reflection, I'm just a pretty flower! Unable to walk, speak, touch, hear, see, taste, love, or live my only dream. Am I truly living?

If I were a chicken, I would sit in my itchy straw nest. It would be uncomfortable laying those hard bumpy eggs. What could I do for fun?! Could I play at a playground? I might not be able to climb the ladder of the slide and I probably would lose some feathers coming down. I'm not sure what would happen to me not on the swings! Could I go swimming? I could fly off the diving board, but I might not be able to swim under the water. How could I get dry again? I think I'd rather be myself.

Hannah Chua, 5

Hannah Chua, Age 5, Orangeville, ON
The Abundant Life School

If I were a chicken, I would sit in my itchy straw nest. It would be uncomfortable laying those hard, bumpy eggs. What could I do for fun?! Could I play at a playground? I might not be able to climb the ladder of the slide, and I probably would lose some feathers coming down. I'm not sure what would happen to me on the swings! Could I go swimming? I could fly off the diving board, but I might not be able to swim under the water. How could I get dry again? I think I'd rather be myself.

If I were a dolphin, I would be friendly and smart. I could swim very fast and flip over very high. Then I could perform at Marineland in the dolphin show. I would be the best dolphin out of all the others and win 1st place in a competition. Also I could have a nice human friend who would always come to watch me swim and talk to me. No other fish would eat me or bite me because I am special. Someday, I could even learn to count or sing like humans. I would be the smartest dolphin ever.

Christine Chung, Age 9

Christine Chung, Age 9, Mississauga, ON
St. Albert of Jerusalem School

If I were a dolphin, I would be friendly and smart. I could swim very fast and flip over very high. Then I could perform at Marineland in the dolphin show. I would be the best dolphin out of all the others and win 1st place in a competition. Also, I could have a nice human friend who would always come to watch me swim and talk to me. No other fish would eat me or bite me because I am special. Someday, I could even learn to count or sing like humans. I would be the smartest dolphin ever.

If I were a kite
I would fly high,
Into the sky.
Up to the moon,
Up to the stars.
Entering heaven, exiting hell.
Drifting along the Milky Way,
Gliding towards Pluto
And passing by Mars.
I would soar just like a falcon,
Looking for prey —
But there's just nothing a kite can say.
I'm a bit like the trees and clouds
Being carried away by the wind.
Up, up, up... and away I flew.
From that day on,
Nobody saw a speck of me
In the daytime views.

Elizabeth Chung, 10

Elizabeth Chung, Age 10, Toronto, ON
Weston Memorial Junior Public School

If I were a kite, I would fly high, into the sky. Up to the moon, up to the stars, entering heaven, exiting hell. Drifting along the Milky Way, gliding toward Pluto, and passing by Mars. I would soar just like a falcon, looking for prey -- but there's just nothing a kite can say. I'm a bit like the trees and clouds, being carried away by the wind. Up, up, up... and away I flew. From that day on, nobody saw a speck of me in the daytime views.

If I were able to become any animal, and able to see how people treat them, I would become them. I would become a bear, and see what it feels like to be forced to dance, just for the entertainment of people. I would become an elephant, and see what it feels like to be killed for my ivory tusks, or, I would become a wolf, and see what it feels like to be constantly driven out of my home by loggers. Not all people are cruel like that, but we need to do something about the people who are.

Maria Cirstea, Age 12

Maria Cirstea, Age 12, Burnaby, BC
Our Lady of Mercy School

If I were able to become any animal, and able to see how people treat them, I would become them. I would become a bear, and see what it feels like to be forced to dance, just for the entertainment of people. I would become an elephant, and see what it feels like to be killed for my ivory tusks, or I would become a wolf, and see what it feels like to be constantly driven out of my home by loggers. Not all people are cruel like that, but we need to do something about the people who are.

If I were able to control the world's resources and countries, I would beseech the people to unite as one to defeat hunger, poverty and strife. I think uniting as one would help in more than this. Countries which have more resources than they need could give them to poorer countries. Scientists could unite in a single lab and find cures for diseases, as well as finding solutions to global warming. All of the educational institutions could join their resources and find the best education methods for teaching and learning. This is my vision.

Ethan Clancy   age 12

Ethan Clancy, Age 12, Calgary, AB
Foundation for the Future Charter Academy

If I were able to control the world's resources and countries, I would beseech the people to unite as one to defeat hunger, poverty and strife. I think uniting as one would help in more than this. Countries which have more resources than they need could give them to poorer countries. Scientists could unite in a single lab and find cures for diseases, as well as finding solutions to global warming. All of the educational institutions could join their resources and find the best education methods for teaching and learning. This is my vision.

If I were an old totem pole, lying in the rain forest, I would tell you of my life. From a sapling, I grew up loving the forest, the chirping birds, and the morning dew. As a mature cedar, I was carved into a beautiful totem pole. A generation later, people that spoke a different language forced my people to abandon their villages and beliefs. Now, after many decades, respect for the old ways is returning. I am lying here, broken, cracked, and decomposing, but still looking at the beauty of Mother Earth through the wise eyes of a thunderbird.

Janelle Collett, Age 11

Janelle Collett, Age 11, Edmonton, AB
St. Benedict School

If I were an old totem pole, lying in the rain forest, I would tell you of my life. From a sapling, I grew up loving the forest, the chirping birds, and the morning dew. As a mature cedar, I was carved into a beautiful totem pole. A generation later people that spoke a different language forced my people to abandon their villages and beliefs. Now, after many decades, respect for the old ways is returning. I am lying here, broken, cracked, and decomposing, but still looking at the beauty of Mother Earth through the wise eyes of a thunderbird.

If I were a dandelion seed I'd sit on my slender stalk and wait until the day a child would pick the dandelion and blow me away. I would start my journey in the child's backyard and then I would sail over the fence and into the park. I'd fly over the laughing children and the clean, sparkling water of the fountain. At the end of the park, I'd blow over a meadow of flowers, birds, and trees. What a beautiful sight! Near the edge of the meadow, a dying wind would urge me to land and start growing up.

Maria R. Collins — 11

Maria R. Collins, Age 11, Mount Pearl, NF
Newtown Elementary School

If I were a dandelion seed, I'd sit on my slender stalk and wait until the day a child would pick the dandelion and blow me away. I would start my journey in the child's backyard, and then I would sail over the fence and into the park. I'd fly over the laughing children and the clean sparkling water of the fountain. At the end of the park, I'd blow over a meadow of flowers, birds, and trees. What a beautiful sight! Near the edge of the meadow, a dying wind would urge me to land and start growing up.

Si j'étais astronaute? Ces astronautes qui, à chaque pas ont une sensation de liberté et qui voient la Terre sous un angle différent du nôtre. Si j'étais astronaute, je m'envolerais à la recherche d'une belle planète et de milliards d'étoiles. Je pourrais même découvrir des créatures bizarres venues d'une galaxie lointaine, très évoluées et qui parleraient dans une langue étrangère. Comme les petits enfants qui rêvent de voyager et de découvrir des milliers de trésors, je reviendrais tellement fière sur la Terre. Pleine de connaissances et au cou, une étoile filante qui porterait chance. Ah! Si j'étais astronaute!

Camila Contreras, 13 ans

Camila Contreras, 13 ans, Montréal, QC
École Louise-Trichet

Si j'étais astronaute? Ces astronautes qui, à chaque pas ont une sensation de liberté et qui voient la Terre sous un angle différent du nôtre. Si j'étais astronaute, je m'envolerais à la recherche d'une belle planète et de milliards d'étoiles. Je pourrais même découvrir des créatures bizarres venues d'une galaxie lointaine, très évoluées et qui parleraient dans une langue étrangère. Comme les petits enfants qui rêvent de voyager et de découvrir des milliers de trésors, je reviendrais tellement fière sur la Terre. Pleine de connaissances et au cou, une étoile filante qui porterait chance. Ah! Si j'étais astronaute!

If I were a piece of trash, I'd be a McDonald's cup. My life would start out by being chosen for someone's drink. "Pick me, pick me! What? She walked right by me!"

Finally one day, I'm picked! "Yippie!" The boy takes me, drinks the pop and throws me onto the street. "Ahhh!"

I get hit by a car. "Ouch! People are so inconsiderate! Can't they swerve around me!"

The wind blows me around. "Yee-haw!" Then it blows me into a dumpster. The garbage man comes and takes us all to rot at the dump, where my life ends!

Courtney Cook, 13

Courtney Cook, Age 13, Hawkestone, ON
East Oro Public School

If I were a piece of trash, I'd be a McDonald's cup. My life would start out by being chosen for someone's drink. "Pick me, pick me! What? She walked right by me!" Finally, one day, I'm picked. "Yippie!" The boy takes me, drinks the pop, and throws me onto the street. "Ahhh!" I get hit by a car. "Ouch! People are so inconsiderate! Can't they swerve around me?" The wind blows me around. "Yee-haw!" Then it blows me into a dumpster. The garbage man comes and takes us all away to rot at the dump, where my life ends.

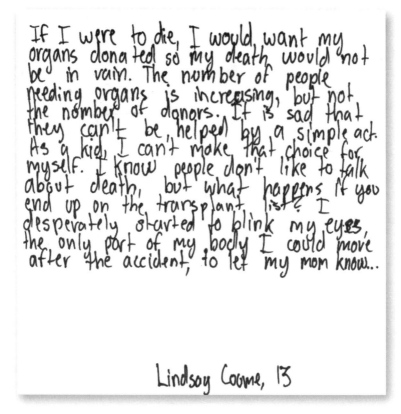

If I were to die, I would want my organs donated so my death would not be in vain. The number of people needing organs is increasing, but not the number of donors. It is sad that they can't be helped by a simple act. As a kid, I can't make that choice for myself. I know people don't like to talk about death, but what happens if you end up on the transplant list? I desperately started to blink my eyes, the only part of my body I could move after the accident, to let my mom know...

Lindsay Coome, 13

Lindsay Coome, Age 13, Unionville, ON
Unionville Public School

If I were to die, I would want my organs donated so my death would not be in vain. The number of people needing organs is increasing, but not the number of donors. It is sad that they can't be helped by a simple act. As a kid, I can't make that choice for myself. I know people don't like to talk about death, but what happens if you end up on the transplant list? I desperately started to blink my eyes, the only part of my body I could move after the accident, to let my mom know...

If I were a dictionary I'd be the smartest one in class. I wouldn't make any spelling mistakes or forgot what a word means. I would know all my antonyms and synonyms without breaking a sweat. I'd tutor after classes and polish my pages. I would always be right and skip a few grades. I'd graduate with honors and be cheered on by many. I'd make a special speech and say these wonderful words that come from inside, literally! Then off to university where I'll teach not study, teach languages to others so that they can become dictionaries like me!

Chloé Corbeil 13

Chloé Corbeil, Age 13, Timmins, ON
École Sacré-Coeur

If I were a dictionary, I'd be the smartest one in class. I wouldn't make any spelling mistakes or forget what a word means. I would know all my antonyms and synonyms without breaking a sweat. I'd tutor after classes and polish my pages. I would always be right and skip a few grades. I'd graduate with honours and be cheered on by many. I'd make a special speech and say these wonderful words that come from inside, literally! Then, off to university where I'll teach, not study, languages to others so that they can become dictionaries like me.

"If I were to go on a pursuit, might I find a ripe juicy fruit?"
Lou was a cheerful little monkey, happy as could be. But the perfect fruit he could not spy.
So into the jungle, Lou set out. The "perfect fruit" was just lying about!
After hours of searching, Lou lost hope, he sat down to mope.
But as he squatted, he kicked a yellow fruit. As he raised it to his lips, and took a bite, the banana was found, on that very night.
Lou prevailed on this feat.
This is how the monkey earned a treat.

Courtney Cunningham Age: 10.

Courtney Cunningham, Age 10, Stratford, ON
Hamlet Public School

"If I were to go on a pursuit, might I find a ripe, juicy fruit?" Lou was a cheerful little monkey, happy as could be. But the perfect fruit, he could not spy. So into the jungle, Lou set out. The 'perfect fruit' was just lying about. After hours of searching, Lou lost hope. He sat down to mope. But as he squatted, he kicked a yellow fruit. As he raised it to his lips and took a bite, the banana was found, on that very night. Lou prevailed on this feat. This is how the monkey earned a treat.

If I were a flying fudge brownie I would find myself a hiding spot and hide in there all day. At night time when everybody is sleeping I would sneak out and fly over to the brownie factory. Once arrived, I would use my magic fudge sleeping powder to make the guards fall asleep, open the doors and scream: Hey brownies, wake up! I'm setting you free! Once all brownies were awake, I would sprinkle flying powder on them so now we can all fly away. Now we are the happiest brownies in the world!

Natasha Daigle, 12.

Natasha Daigle, Age 12, Saint John, NB
Samuel de Champlain School

If I were a flying fudge brownie, I would find myself a hiding spot and hide in there all day. At night time, when everybody is sleeping, I would sneak out and fly over to the brownie factory. Once arrived, I would use my magic fudge sleeping powder to make the guards fall asleep, open the door and scream: "Hey, brownies! Wake up! I'm setting you free!" Once all brownies were awake, I would sprinkle flying powder on them so now, we can all fly away. Now we are the happiest brownies in the world!

If I were a stoplight I'd be king of my hill. I'd be an emotional yet tactful leader. Accidents would rarely happen when I'm around. But, on my throne, emotions would run high. I'd get green with envy of cars, the lower being, who are able to move at their own free will. I'd get embarrassed. Having all eyes on you is not always easy. I'd also get scared. Scared to make a mistake that could be fatal. I am slightly yellow-bellied However, I am a powerful leader. Everyone knows this and few dare to rebel.

Shannon Dalley, 13

Shannon Dalley, Age 13, New Glasgow, NS
East Pictou School

If I were a stoplight, I'd be king of my hill. I'd be an emotional, yet tactful leader. Accidents would rarely happen when I'm around. But, on my throne, emotions would run high. I'd get green with envy of cars, the lower being, who are able to move at their own free will. I'd get embarrassed. Having all eyes on you is not always easy. I'd also get scared, scared to make a mistake that could be fatal. I am slightly yellow-bellied. However, I am a powerful leader. Everyone knows this, and few dare to rebel.

If I were to sprout wings I'd fly to the man in the moon. I'd soar past the shooting stars and Drink the Milky Way. I'd dive down back to earth and soar with the laughing gulls. I would fly over the ocean and watch the rolling waves. I'd fly down cliffs and laugh with the wind in my face. I'd fly past trees and count the leaves. Even before the day was done, I'd go to sleep and dream of flying, at the very first sunrise, or even at the crack of dawn!

Gabrielle Dao, 11.

Gabrielle Dao, Age 11, New Westminster, BC
Our Lady of Mercy School

If I were to sprout wings, I'd fly to the man in the moon. I'd soar past the shooting stars and drink the Milky Way. I'd dive down back to Earth and soar with the laughing gulls. I would fly over the ocean and watch the rolling waves. I'd fly down cliffs and laugh with the wind in my face. I'd fly past trees and count the leaves. Even before the day was done, I'd go to sleep and dream of flying, at the very first sunrise, or even at the crack of dawn!

65

If I were a gremlin
I'd hide in someones shoe.
And if they stuck their toes in
I wouldn't know what to do.
I maybe try to bite them,
I maybe try to hide,
but if they stuck them farther,
I'd run to the other side.
I maybe growl a little
or maybe shriek a howl.
But if they try to step on me
what will I do now?
I'll run up his pants on to his shirt,
"Oh, what's that I see?
He's eating desert!"
I'll sneak a bite,
When time is right
and hope he won't see me.
          Melissa Darbyson   age: 10

Melissa Darbyson, Age 10, Corbeil, ON
Ferris Glen School

If I were a gremlin, I'd hide in someone's shoe. And if they stuck their toes in, I wouldn't know what to do. I'd maybe try to bite them, I'd maybe try and hide, but if they stuck them farther, I'd run to the other side. I'd maybe growl a little, or maybe shriek or howl, but if they try to step on me, what will I do now? I'd run up his pants, onto his shirt. Oh, what's that I see? He's eating dessert! I'll sneak a bite when the time is right, and hope he won't see me.

Si j'étais un chat, j'aimerais monter sur les plus hautes armoires de la cuisine et me faire flatter pendant longtemps à tous les jours. J'aimerais avoir accès à la chambre de mon maître pour pouvoir aller dans son lit. Je voudrais manger de la nourriture de première qualité et habiter dans une maison où il y a plein de divans et de coussins. Je voudrais être le seul animal de la maison pour que les personnes s'occupent plus de moi. J'aimerais jouer à la balle avec mon maître. Mais je préfère beaucoup mieux être un humain comme je suis présentement !

Marie-Ève Deslauriers 10 ans

Marie-Ève Deslauriers, 10 ans,
Cap-de-la-Madeleine, QC
École Monseigneur Comtois

Si j'étais un chat, j'aimerais monter sur les plus hautes armoires de la cuisine et me faire flatter pendant longtemps à tous les jours. J'aimerais avoir accès à la chambre de mon maître pour pouvoir aller dans son lit. Je voudrais manger de la nourriture de première qualité et habiter dans une maison où il y a plein de divans et de coussins. Je voudrais être le seul animal de la maison pour que les personnes s'occupent plus de moi. J'aimerais jouer à la balle avec mon maître. Mais je préfère beaucoup mieux être un humain comme je suis présentement!

"If I were a child, how would life be?" Thought Jonathan the cat. Jonathan was a cat who was bored with his life. He wanted to be like children. "Children can do anything. They're active, and their lives are more exciting then mine. My owner is a child, so I could play with her. But Sarah does get into trouble when she does something wrong. That would mean I couldn't go out at night and play with my buddies. And that I won't keep my beautiful fur coat. Maybe I'll stay a cat and play with children, not be one!"

Victoria Di Giovanni Age 11

Victoria Di Giovanni, Age 11, Thornhill, ON
St. Joseph The Worker Catholic School

"If I were a child, how would life be?" thought Jonathan the cat. Jonathan was a cat who was bored with his life. He wanted to be like children. "Children can do anything. They're active, and their lives are more exciting than mine. My owner is a child, so I could play with her. But Sarah does not get into trouble when she does something wrong. That would mean I couldn't go out at night and play with my buddies. And that I won't keep my beautiful fur coat. Maybe I'll stay a cat and play with children, not be one!"

If I were an ocean, I would be like a silky cover protecting the majestic creatures who would dwell beneath my surface. The dolphins would gracefully jump over me outlined by the setting sun, while my waves beat gently on the shore. The crisp evening breeze would ripple my surface while the reflection of the night sky would give the illusion of fallen stars. Sigh, as graceful as it is, I will never compare to the beauty of the ocean. For I am simply sand. Of no beauty, elegance or grace, consumed by the beauty that I will never become.

Daniela DiPaolo   12

Daniela DiPaolo, Age 12, Richmond Hill, ON
Oak Ridges Public School

If I were an ocean, I would be like a silk cover protecting the majestic creatures who would dwell beneath my surface. The dolphins would gracefully jump over me, outlined by the setting sun, while my waves beat gently on the shore. The crisp evening breeze would ripple my surface, while the reflection of the night sky would give the illusion of fallen stars. Sigh, as graceful as it is, I will never compare to the beauty of the ocean. For I am simply sand, of no beauty, elegance or grace, consumed by the beauty that I will never become.

If I were a story, I would be about a big, long-earred hippo named Candace. Candace always slipped on her ears because they were so long. She had to get an ear cut. She cried and cried for the whole time at the vet. She had to take a sleeping pill to help her sleep good while her ears were being cut. She did not cry and cry when she was asleep. When she woke up, her ears were short and did not slip anymore. That is what my author would write about if I were a story.

Cecilia Dobek, 5

Cecilia Dobek, Age 5, Calgary, AB
Home-schooled

If I were a story, I would be about a big, long-earred hippo named Candace. Candace always slipped on her ears because they were so long. She had to get an ear cut. She cried and cried for the whole time at the vet. She had to take a sleeping pill to help her sleep good while her ears were being cut. She did not cry and cry when she was asleep. When she woke up, her ears were short and did not slip anymore. That is what my author would write about if I were a story.

Si j'étais auteure, j'inventerais des personnages curieux et attachants. Mes histoires seraient composées de tendresse, d'amour et de suspense. Le tout serait bien encadré dans un monde réel. Tout ça serait le fruit de mon imagination. Je ferais de mon mieux pour que mes livres soient gratuits et passionants. Les animations concernant mes livres seraient agrémentées d'une touche de farfelu et de quelques bribes d'histoires de mon cru. À ces occasions, je remettrais mes livres à des enfants pour favoriser le goût de la lecture et de l'écriture. Mon rêve se concrétisera peut-être un jour...

Ève Doré-Véronneau   12 ans

Ève Doré-Véronneau, 12 ans, Sainte-Julienne, QC
École Havre-Jeunesse

Si j'étais auteure, j'inventerais des personnages curieux et attachants. Mes histoires seraient composées de tendresse, d'amour et de suspense. Le tout serait bien encadré dans un monde réel. Tout ça serait le fruit de mon imagination. Je ferais de mon mieux pour que mes livres soient gratuits et passionnants. Les animations concernant mes livres seraient agrémentées d'une touche de farfelu et de quelques bribes d'histoires de mon cru. À ces occasions, je remettrais mes livres à des enfants pour favoriser le goût de la lecture et de l'écriture. Mon rêve se concrétisera peur-être un jour...

If I were a dollar I'd be used, and re-used, never ceasing, I'd be put in a bank, I'd be spent on a car, or on shoes. I'd have many owners both good, and bad, happy, and sad. I'd be used to buy junk, I'd be used to buy treasure. I'd be put in a purse to collect dust for years, or until another adventure would quite suddenly arise. Sometimes I'd be found, and I'd put a smile on a face. But wherever I'd go I'd always be wanted, and always be lovingly cherished, and everyone would be my friend.

Jennifer Doucet age 12

Jennifer Doucet, Age 12, Mississauga, ON
René-Lamoureux School

If I were a dollar I'd be used and reused, never ceasing. I'd be put in a bank, I'd be spent on a car, or on shoes. I'd have many owners, both good and bad, happy and sad. I'd be used to buy junk, I'd be used to buy treasure. I'd be put in a purse to collect dust for years, or until another adventure would quite suddenly arise. Sometimes I'd be found, and I'd put a smile on a face. But wherever I'd go, I'd always be wanted, and always be lovingly cherished, and everyone would be my friend.

If I were a time traveller,
the first thing I Would do is to
go back to ancient Greece to
see the very first Olympics. Or,
maybe visit ancient Egypt to
solve some of the greatest
Egyptian mysteries. I would
make my summer holidays last
forever! Soon, I Would go to
the future to see what challenges
lie ahead, What perils must be
faced. I'd ask questions like," Will
there be Earth - colonies on
Mars? Will all diseases have a
cure? Will Earth still exist?
What other, planets might be
discovered?"
I wonder?

Jeremy Doucet

Jeremy Doucet, Age 11, Bathurst, NB
Superior Middle School

If I were a time traveller, the first thing I would do is to go back to ancient Greece to see the very first Olympics. Or maybe visit ancient Egypt to solve some of the greatest Egyptian mysteries! I would make my summer holidays last forever! Soon, I would go to the future to see what challenges lie ahead, what perils must be faced. I'd ask questions like "Will there be Earth colonies on Mars? Will all diseases have a cure? Will Earth still exist? What other planets might be discovered?" I wonder.

Si j'étais... un écureuil, je grimperais aux arbres et je pourrais courir partout. Si j'étais un écureuil gris, je pourrais ainsi me camoufler aux arbres, si j'étais un écureuil roux, le monde aurait moins peur de moi que si j'étais un écureuil noir. Si j'étais un écureuil scaphandre, je pourrais nager librement de tous les écureuils que je préférerais être c'est l'écureuil volant, car voler est un de mes grands rêves

Simon Dubé 12

Simon Dubé, 12 ans, St-Eustache, QC
Externat Sacré-Cœur

Si j'étais un écureuil, je grimperais aux arbres et je pourrais courir partout. Si j'étais un écureuil gris, je pourrais ainsi me camoufler aux arbres. Si j'étais un écureuil roux, le monde aurait moins peur de moi que si j'étais un écureuil noir. Si j'étais un écureuil scaphandre, je pourrais nager librement sans me faire attaquer. Mais de tous les écureuils que je préférerais être, c'est l'écureuil volant, car voler est un de mes grands rêves.

Si j'étais ...le soleil, j'éclairerais tous les visages pour que personne ne soit perdu ou oublié. Si j'étais la lune, je bercerais tous les enfants qui ont fait de mauvais rêves. Si j'étais une étoile, j'exaucerais tous les bons voeux. Si j'étais le vent, je soufflerais aux oreilles des gens ce qu'ils voudraient entendre. Si j'étais la mer, je porterais les vagues au bord de la plage. Si j'étais une étincelle, je ferais briller les yeux, pour qu'une lueur les rende heureux. J'aimerais être un arc-en-ciel pour voir un sourire s'afficher sur chaque visage. Si j'étais la paix, je règnerais.

Catherine Dutrisac 12 ans

Catherine Dutrisac, 12 ans, Hull, QC
Collège St-Joseph de Hull

Si j'étais le soleil, j'éclairerais tous les visages pour que personne ne soit perdu ou oublié. Si j'étais la lune, je bercerais tous les enfants qui ont fait de mauvais rêves. Si j'étais une étoile, j'exaucerais tous les bons vœux. Si j'étais le vent, je soufflerais aux oreilles des gens ce qu'ils voudraient entendre. Si j'étais la mer, je porterais les vagues au bord de la plage. Si j'étais une étincelle, je ferais briller les yeux, pour qu'une lueur les rende heureux. J'aimerais être un arc-en-ciel pour voir un sourire s'afficher sur chaque visage. Si j'étais la paix, je règnerais.

Si j'étais musicienne je jouerais de la trompette. Si j'étais musicienne je jouerais du tambour. Si j'étais musicienne je jouerais de la guitare et du piano avec mes parents. Si J'étais musicienne je jouerais peut-être dans une fanfare. Si j'étais musicienne, peut-être que ma musique jouerait à la radio, peut-être même à la télévision. Si j'étais musicienne, c'est sûr que j'ourais pleins d'instruments de musique chez moi et j'inviterais tous mes amis à venir en jouer avec moi. Si j'étais musicienne, je voudrais jouer de la musique dehors devant pleins de gens qui nous applaudiraient moi et tous mes amis.

Emmanuelle-Jade Duval 4½ ans

Emmanuelle-Jade Duval, 4 ans, Warwick, QC
CPE La forêt enchantée

Si j'étais musicienne, je jouerais de la trompette. Si j'étais musicienne, je jouerais du tambour. Si j'étais musicienne, je jouerais de la guitare et du piano avec mes parents. Si j'étais musicienne, je jouerais peut-être dans une fanfare. Si j'étais musicienne, peut-être que ma musique jouerait à la radio, peut-être même à la télévision. Si j'étais musicienne, c'est sûr que j'aurais plein d'instruments de musique chez moi et j'inviterais tous mes amis à venir en jouer avec moi. Si j'étais musicienne, je voudrais jouer de la musique dehors devant plein de gens qui nous applaudiraient moi et tous mes amis.

If I were able to heal a wound, with only one touch of my hand, I would do so.
If I could cure a sickness, with only one tear from my eye, I would do so.
If I could bring back the dead, by preying day and night, I would do so.
If I could stop wars, by only using my voice, instead of weapons to harm, I would do so.
And if people would listen to what everyone has to say, the earth would be a much better place!!!

Victoria Ellison 10

Victoria Ellison, Age 10, Lower Sackville, NS
Millwood Elementary School

If I were able to heal a wound, with only one touch of my hand,
I would do so. If I could cure a sickness with only one tear from my
eye, I would do so. If I could bring back the dead by praying day and
night, I would do so. If I could stop wars by only using my voice,
instead of weapons to harm, I would do so. And if people would listen
to what everyone has to say, the Earth would be a much better place!

IF I WeRe A Doger I WOULD BE A vet BeCAUSe I LOVe ALL ANIMALS. I WOULD tAKe cAre oF every tyPe oF ANIMAL, eveN DUCKs, CAts ANd tiGers ANd BeArs WHo GOt SICK At tHe ZOO. oNE DAY WHILE I WAs rUBBING A SICK tiGers tUMMY He stArteD to LAUGH. I DIDN4 KNoW tiGers were tICKLISH. I tICKLeD every SiNGLe ANIMAL tHey ALL stArted to GiGGLe. I MADe tHeM Better BY MAKING tHeM LAUGH. ALL tHe ANIMALs FeLL ASLeeP ANd I WAs FINISHED FOR tHe DAY. tHe eND.

ISABEL EStABrOoK 4 yrs.

Isabel Estabrook, Age 4, Nepean, ON
Churchill Alternative School

If I were a doctor, I would be a vet because I love all animals. I would take care of every type of animal, even ducks, cats and tigers, and bears who got sick at the zoo. One day while I was rubbing a sick tiger's tummy, he started to laugh. I didn't know tigers were ticklish. I tickled every single animal. They all started to giggle. I made them better by making them laugh. All the animals fell asleep and I was finished for the day. The End.

If I were a great blue heron, I would walk along the rocky shore, then say good morning to the purple starfish. I'd listen to the wind whistling in my face and feel the waves rolling against my feet. I would love the dark blue sea. Some days I would find a big rock to stand on and just stare out at the sea. I would wonder if it was going to be here forever, for everyone to enjoy. And I hope that everyone would take good care of it as much as me.

Rosemary Fairweather, 10

Rosemary Fairweather, Age 10, Lantzville, BC
Seaview Elementary School

If I were a great blue heron, I would walk along the rocky shore, then say good morning to the purple starfish. I'd listen to the wind whistling in my face, and feel the waves rolling against my feet. I would love the dark blue sea. Some days I would find a big rock to stand on, and just stare out at the sea. I would wonder if it was going to be here forever, for everyone to enjoy. And I hope that everyone would take good care of it, as much as me.

If I were a gentle breeze
I would blow to new lands
and try to answer every
wish I can. I would blow
across little kids faces to
make them feel better.
When it was winter I
Would freeze the water
so little kids could skate
on it. I would pick up kites
so they would sail up to the
sky. But most of all I
could see many different
places because I would be
invisible so I could go in
different houses. I just
think being the wind for
a few days would be fun.
Christie Felker, age 8

Christie Felker, Age 8, Brantford, ON
Mount Pleasant School

If I were a gentle breeze, I would blow to new lands and try to answer
every wish I can. I would blow across little kids faces to make them
feel better. When it was winter, I would freeze the water so little kids
could skate on it. I would pick up kites so they would sail up to the
sky. But most of all, I could see many different places because I would
be invisible, so I could go in different houses. I just think being the
wind for a few days would be fun.

If I were a Gabula I would have to be extremely cautious, because no human must ever see a Gabula. Gabula's have brown fuzzy fur covering their plump little bodies. They only come out after dark. Why, you ask? Well their main diet is nutritious apple juice. They stretch their stubby legs to three metres, pick an apple off a tree and bite it in half. Then they rub the delicious juices on their scrawney little arms, and by moonlight absorb it. So you wonder how I know so much about Gabula's? Well, you see, I am an Apple tree.

Heidi Franks, 12

Heidi Franks, Age 12, Peterborough, ON
James Strath Public School

If I were a Gabula I would have to be extremely cautious, because no human must ever see a Gabula. Gabulas have brown fuzzy fur covering their plump little bodies. They only come out after dark. Why, you ask? Well their main diet is nutritious apple juice. They stretch their stubby legs to three metres, pick an apple off a tree and bite it in half. Then they rub the delicious juices on their scrawny little arms, and by moonlight, absorb it. So you wonder how I know so much about Gabulas? Well, you see I am an apple tree.

If I were a magician it would be too easy to make a rabbit come out of my hat I would make a hedgehog come out of my mitten would my assistant be a pretty lady? No, mine would be my brother complete with a feather boa. TA DA. You have seen other magicians cut people in two? I would slice a cake in two. I would eat one side and share the rest with the audience. THE BEST PART OF being a magician is if my brother bothered me I could make him disappear. POOP!!

MIKAYLA FRY, 5

Mikayla Fry, Age 5, Oakville, ON
Westoak Public School

If I were a magician, it would be too easy to make a rabbit come out of my hat. I would make a hedgehog come out of my mitten. Would my assistant be a pretty lady? No, mine would be my brother complete with a feather boa. TA DA! You have seen other magicians cut people in two? I would slice a cake in two. I would eat one side and share the rest with the audience. The best part of being a magician is if my brother bothered me, I could make him disappear. POOF!

If I were ... a cloud ... I'd be the cloud of happiness and joy. I'd be a cloud light as a feather! I'd travel all the lands from North America to Asia spreading raindrops of peace and harmony upon all the vast lands! By the time I was done everyone would be working as one, hand in hand. Thus something like nine/eleven would never happen again! If only such a thing would come true everyone would be happy like me and you! If peace and love were at the top of the list no one would ever raise a fist!

Jelena Gacesa   age 12

Jelena Gacesa, Age 12, Tecumseh, ON
A.V. Graham School

If I were a cloud... I'd be the cloud of happiness and joy. I'd be a cloud light as a feather! I'd travel all the lands from North America to Asia, spreading raindrops of peace and harmony upon all the vast lands! By the time I was done, everyone would be working as one, hand in hand. Thus, something like 9/11 would never happen again! If only such a thing would come true, everyone would be happy, like me and you! If peace and love were at the top of the list, no one would ever raise a fist!

> If I were a comet I would travel the univers roaming the galaxies while visiting each planet and star. I would fly accross the asteroid fields and dash through the sky to amaze people with my blinding light and my long shiny tail. I would race against the space shuttles and visite the astronauts from time to time. Each and every day of fun would be just another day in outer space. Every single day, I would shrink and shrink until I become nothing but dust...

David Gagnon 10

David Gagnon, Age 10, Ottawa, ON
École de Cumberland

If I were a comet I would travel the universe roaming the galaxies while visiting each planet and star. I would fly across the asteroid fields and dash through the sky to amaze people with my blinding light and my long shiny tail. I would spin around the moon and soar in the heat of the sun. I would race against the space shuttles and visit the astronauts from time to time. Each and every day of fun would be just another day in outer space. Every single day, I would shrink and shrink until I become nothing but dust…

Darcy Gale, Age 11, Doyle, NF
Belanger School

If I were my mom I could see World War II. I would be able to be in
Germany and know some German. My mom still knows some
German, like one to ten. I would also see how long it takes to travel
from Germany to Canada, and see all of the places she saw. I would
be in British Columbia, at her wedding. I would even own a nursery
called 'Valley Nursery'. I would have four children. And be old
enough to drive. I would drive to Stephenville or Cornerbrook,
delivering flowers. I wish I were my mom!

If I were a firefighter I would save lives. I would have been there on September eleventh two thousand and one. I think firefighters are very significant in our world. I think they are heros. I would like to be a hero so that people would look up to me. I think firefighters are a very good influence on kids. I would always be there whenever and wherever the emergency is. I would get lots of rewards that say "In Honor Of Bravery and strength." I would be the very best firefighter in the whole entire universe.

By: Erica Gallipoli, 9

Erica Gallipoli, Age 9, Toronto, ON
St. Fidelis Catholic School

If I were a firefighter, I would save lives. I would have been there on September 11th, 2001. I think firefighters are very significant in our world. I think they are heroes. I would like to be a hero so that people would look up to me. I think firefighters are a very good influence on kids. I would always be there whenever and wherever the emergency is. I would get lots of rewards that say 'In Honour of Bravery and Strength.' I would be the very best firefighter in the whole entire universe.

If I were ... my favourite book I don't think that I would ever be bored. I would always have an adventure waiting for me with the turn of a page. First I would go on a journey across the ocean where I would face fierce storms, then I would land in an exotic country with a different culture. There I would encounter fastinating creatures and people that would influence my life forever. I would try new foods and make new friends. After my adventures I'd take a ride home on a rainbow and have a rest before my next adventure.

Alexsandra Anna Gieralt   12

Aleksandra Anna Gierat, Age 12, London, ON
Blessed Sacrament Catholic School

If I were my favourite book, I don't think that I would ever be bored. I would always have an adventure waiting for me with the turn of a page. First, I would go on a journey across the ocean, where I would face fierce storms, then I would land in an exotic country with a different culture. There I would encounter fascinating creatures and people that would influence my life forever. I would try new foods and make new friends. After my adventures, I'd take a ride home on a rainbow and have a rest before my next adventure.

If I were a star... but the skies are filled with stars, none more noticed than the next. Except for one. Viewing all the ages of the world pass beneath my glow, I play no part in history, being merely a spectator. But I was a compass in times past, the guiding light to travellers shrouded by darkness and invoked with fear. Sitting atop the heavens, I could watch and listen to the world as the one star that holds its place. If I were the North Star.

Lauren Gordon, 12

Lauren Gordon, Age 12, Thornhill, ON
PACE

If I were a star… but the skies are filled with stars, none more noticed than the next. Except for one. Viewing all the ages of the world pass beneath my glow, I play no part in history, being merely a spectator. But I was a compass in times past, the guiding light to travellers shrouded by darkness and envoked with fear. Sitting atop the heavens, I could watch and listen to the world as the one star that holds its place. If I were the North Star.

If I were a fairy godmother, I would grant wishes and create peace on our planet. Every day would be magical. People would ride the rainbow, find the pot of gold, and talk to the animals. There would be food for all. Books, music and laughter would be shared. The garden fairies would keep nature alive. People would stay healthy. It is magical to wish, dream and hope.

Melanie Grauds, age 9

Melanie Grauds, Age 9, North York, ON
Yorkview Public School

If I were a fairy godmother, I would grant wishes and create peace on our planet. Every day would be magical. People would ride the rainbow, find the pot of gold, and talk to the animals. There would be food for all. Books, music and laughter would be shared. The garden fairies would keep nature alive. People would stay healthy. It is magical to wish, dream and hope.

If I were... a water molecule, I would be part of the Hydrologic Cycle. In this progressing cycle, I wouldn't get to choose where I start. Ahh... There's no time to choose. I'm already falling as a droplet of rain! Oh no, I'm just about to dive into a fast running river and here come some Kayakers too! Uh, they just flattened me like a pancake. Slurp, slurp. Awww, great! I'm just about to be licked up by a moose, and here I go! It's like an indoor roller coaster! I'm going to the bladder and down into the underworld!

Brandon Greenside, 12

Brandon Greenside, Age 12, London, ON
M.B. McEachren School

If I were a water molecule, I would be part of the hydrologic cycle. In this progressing cycle, I wouldn't get to choose where I start. Ahhhh ... there's no time to choose. I'm already falling as a droplet of rain! Oh no, I'm just about to dive into a fast-running river, and here come some kayakers too! Uh, they just flattened me like a pancake, slurp, slurp. Awww, great! I'm just about to be licked up by a moose, and here I go! It's like an indoor roller coaster! I'm going to the bladder and down into the underworld!

Si j'étais... un Papillon, je Partirais à la conquête des pays chauds. Je virevolterais dans le ciel bleu. Quand je trouverais cet endroit, j'y ferais venir ma colonie. Pour cela, j'y consacrerais tout le temps qu'il faudrait. Je prendrais bien garde à moi, en passant au dessus du volcan Santa Ana, du Salvador. Les papillons sont frasiles. En arrivant en Colombie, je profiterais de me faire dorer au soleil sur les plages de cartagena. Peut-être que j'arrêterais mon périple a Bogota. Pendant ce parcours, je ferais voir à tout le monde les splendides couleurs des mes ailts.

Marie-Gaelle Grenier   9ans

Marie-Gaelle Grenier, 9 ans, St-Germain, QC
École Roméo-Salois

Si j'étais un papillon, je partirais à la conquête des pays chauds. Je virevolterais dans le ciel bleu. Quand je trouverais cet endroit, j'y ferais venir ma colonie. Pour cela, j'y consacrerais tout le temps qu'il faudrait. Je prendrais bien garde à moi, en passant au-dessus du volcan Santa Ana, du Salvador. Les papillons sont fragiles. En arrivant en Colombie, je profiterais de me faire dorer au soleil sur les plages de Cartagena. Peut-être que j'arrêterais mon périple à Bogota. Pendant ce parcours, je ferais voir à tout le monde les splendides couleurs de mes ailes.

If I were... a water lily I would open up to the sun every morning, eager to watch the day go by without a care in the world. I would drift along peacefully on a pond, every now and then letting a frog stop by to rest or say hello.

When it rained, I would close up, not wanting to face the day. But that wouldn't be so bad, just laying there on my padded bed.

At night, if it was truly impossible to avoid, I would stare up at the sky, without a thought except how beautiful my life was.

Maria Halavrezos, age 11

Maria Halavrezos, Age 11, Dartmouth, NS
Hawthorn Elementary School

If I were a water lily I would open up to the sun every morning, eager to watch the day go by without a care in the world. I would drift along peacefully on a pond, every now and then letting a frog stop by to rest or say hello. When it rained, I would close up, not wanting to face the day. But that wouldn't be so bad, just laying on my padded bed. At night, if it was truly impossible to avoid, I would stare up at the sky, without a thought except how beautiful my life was.

If I were a wolf, I would want to be winged, like Alina, a magical female wolf in the land of Kiradell. Her smokey black fur and flame-like markings represent the element of fire. She wears an amulet with a gem in the shape of a flame. This amulet holds powers that enlighten her gift of speed and strength. This amulet was given to her by a fairy. who also gave an Amulet of Light to her mate, Eclipse, who is the leader of the pack. Together, they lead the wolf pack to victory against evil in their land, Kiradell.

Kayla Hamilton, age 11.

Kayla Hamilton, Age 11, Delta, BC
English Bluff Elementary School

If I were a wolf, I would want to be winged, like Alina, a magical female wolf in the land of Kiradell. Her smokey black fur and flame-like markings represent the element of fire. She wears an amulet with a gem in the shape of a flame. The amulet holds powers that enlighten her gift of speed and strength. This amulet was given to her by a fairy who also gave an amulet of light to her mate, Eclipse, who is the leader of the pack. Together, (they lead) the wolf pack to victory against evil in their land, Kiradell.

If I were to achieve my greatest dreams, I would be sharing with the world my love, life and being, through writing and song. My poetry would show my emotions, my music would describe my soul, and my lifestyle would always share my faith. My inspiration would be my heart, and what it is feeling. It's simply amazing what you can do when you listen to your heart's voice instead of making your mind say what you want it to say. So, my best advice to you is "Love, live, learn, listen, and you will complete all of your dreams.

Courtney Harris, 13

Courtney Harris, Age 13, Coldbrook, NS
Coldbrook & District School

If I were to achieve my greatest dreams, I would be sharing with the world my love, life, and being through writing and song. My poetry would show my emotions, my music would describe my soul, and my lifestyle would always share my faith. My inspiration would be my heart and what it is feeling. It's simply amazing what you can do when you listen to your heart's voice, instead of making your mind say what you want it to say. So, my best advice to you is "love, live, learn, listen, and you will complete all of your dreams."

If I were the wind on a dark stormy day,
I would blow all the hats of the people away.

I would blow the sea's waves up onto the shore,
and I'd blow and I'd blow 'till I could blow nomore.

I'd rattle the windows of the houses on the street,
and I'd ruffle the gardens, that looked so neat.

I would blow myself into such a frightful gale,
I'd whistle and bellow, howl, shriek, scream and wail.

Then the clouds would part and the sun would shine,
and I'd be the breeze.

(Until next time.)

Alyssa Hauer   age 11

Alyssa Hauer, Age 11, Vancouver, BC
York House School

If I were the wind on a dark stormy day, I would blow all the hats of the
people away. I would blow the sea's waves up onto the shore, and I'd
blow, and I'd blow, 'til I could blow no more. I'd rattle the windows of
the houses on the street, and I'd ruffle the gardens that looked so neat.
I would blow myself into such a frightful gale, I'd whistle and bellow,
howl, shriek, scream and wail! Then the clouds would part, and the sun
would shine, and I'd be the breeze (until next time).

If I were the northern lights, I would shimmer and glimmer and shine so brightly I would light up the sky. My colors would flicker and dance. People would come out of their homes just to watch my graceful performance. I would bring a smile to every unhappy person's face, their eyes reflecting off my every move. Their breath would catch in their throats as they beheld my elegance. And as the sky began to gradually lighten I would slowly and smoothly melt away like butter. People would sigh and go home to wait in anticipation for my next appearance.

Lindsay Haverslew 13

Lindsay Haverslew, Age 13, Vermilion, AB
J.R. Robson School

If I were the northern lights, I would shimmer and glimmer and shine so brightly I would light up the sky. My colours would flicker and dance. People would come out of their houses just to watch my graceful performance. I would bring a smile to every unhappy person's face, their eyes reflecting off my every move. Their breath would catch in their throats as they beheld my elegance. And as the sky began to gradually lighten I would slowly and smoothly melt away like butter. People would sigh and go home, to wait in anticipation for my next appearance.

If I were a shooting star I would soar through outer space. I would travel all around the galaxy so children everywhere could look up at me and make their wishes, "I wish for a soccer ball, a teddybear, a doll or a doll house!" they would exclaim. I would try my hardest to make every one of their wishes come true. It would make me feel great to make all of those children very, very happy. I would do all of that if I were a shooting star, but then again, I like being exactly who I really am!

Erika Heidebrecht, age 11

Erika Heidebrecht, Age 11, Ottawa, ON
Elmdale Public School

If I were a shooting star, I would soar through outer space. I would travel all around the galaxy so children everywhere could look up at me and make their wishes. "I wish for a soccer ball, a teddy bear, a doll or a doll house!" they would exclaim. I would try my hardest to make every one of their wishes come true. It would make me feel great to make all of those children very very happy. I would do all of that if I were a shooting star, but then again, I like being exactly who I really am!

Si j'étais un chercheur de médicaments, j'inventerais le médicament du cancer et je serais milliardaire!... Dans le sous-sol de ma maison, ce serait un immense laboratoire de chimie contenant des éprouvettes, des bouteilles de potions inventées par moi. J'utiliserais un ordinateur sophistiqué, un microscope très perfectionné. Vêtu d'un long sarrau et des gants pour me protéger contre les produits toxiques. Je passerais de longs moments à chercher, chercher pour enfin trouver les médicaments qui soulageront les gens. Finalement, les personnes guéries par mes recherches seraient mes invités dans mon superbe camp de pêche et je serais je plus heureux!

si mon-Hérard 11 ans

Simon Hérard, 11 ans, Shawinigan-Sud, QC
École Saint-Paul

Si j'étais un chercheur de médicaments, j'inventerais le médicament
du cancer et je serais milliardaire! Dans le sous-sol de ma maison, ce serait
un immense laboratoire de chimie contenant des éprouvettes, des bouteilles
de potions inventées par moi. J'utiliserais un ordinateur sophistiqué, un
microscope très perfectionné. Vêtu d'un long sarrau et des gants pour me
protéger contre les produits toxiques, je passerais de longs moments à
chercher, chercher pour enfin trouver les médicaments qui soulageront les
gens. Finalement, les personnes guéries par mes recherches seraient mes
invités dans mon superbe camp de pêche et je serais le plus heureux!

If I were a Hammerhead shark, I
would swim in a swimming pool.
It would be hot. I would love catching
fish in the sea. I would like to have
an adventure in the sea. I would be
chasing a fish. I wouldeat the fish until
it was gone. A guy was fishing in the
sea when he caught a great white
shark. The shark pulled him in the
sea. The white shark ate him up and
the great white shark fought with a
hammer head shark. The great white
shark lost! The hammerhead was the
victor. I love hammer head sharks!

Nathanelle Hiebert, 6

Nathanelle Hiebert, Age 6, Sexsmith, AB
Families Learning Together

If I were a Hammerhead shark, I would swim in a swimming pool.
It would be hot. I would love catching fish in the sea. I would like to
have an adventure in the sea. I would be chasing a fish. I would eat
the fish until it was gone. A guy was fishing in the sea when he caught
a Great White shark. The shark pulled him in the sea. The white shark
ate him up, and the Great White shark fought with a Hammerhead
shark. The Great White shark lost! The Hammerhead was the victor.
I love Hammerhead sharks!

If I were perfect, my hair wouldn't be too curly or too straight. My legs wouldn't be too long or too short. My skin wouldn't be too dark or too light. If I were perfect, my decisions would always be correct. If I were perfect, I wouldn't learn from my mistakes, and I would find faults in all my friends. I would have the perfect family, my sister and I would get along. If I were perfect, I wouldn't be criticized, but then I couldn't improve either. If I were perfect, I would be boring and I wouldn't be me.

— Nicole Hingston, 13

Nicole Hingston, Age 13, Guelph, ON
Sacred Heart School

If I were perfect, my hair wouldn't be too curly or too straight. My legs wouldn't be too long or too short. My skin wouldn't be too dark or too light. If I were perfect, my decisions would always be correct. If I were perfect, I wouldn't learn from my mistakes, and I would find faults in all my friends. I would have the perfect family, my sister and I would get along. If I were perfect, I wouldn't be criticized, but then I couldn't improve either. If I were perfect, I would be boring, and I wouldn't be me.

If I were an astronaut
this is what I'd do,
fly around the earth and
bring two friends too.

If I were a bird,
this is what I'd do,
I would fly around town
looking for some food.
If I were an ape
this is what I'd do,
I would swing on the vines in the
jungle or the zoo.

If I were a boy what
would I do? I'd write you this
story and now it is through.

Brent Holland, 8 yrs.

Brent Holland, Age 8, Williams Lake, BC
Poplar Glade School

If I were an astronaut this is what I'd do, fly around the Earth and
bring two friends too. If I were a bird, this is what I'd do, I would fly
around town looking for some food. If I were an ape this is what I'd
do, I would swing on the vines in the jungle or the zoo. If I were a
boy what would I do? I'd write you this story and now it is through.

Si j'etais... la reine du monde tout le monde dépenderais sur moi. J'habiterais dans un château et j'aurais des pandas, des chattes, et des chevaux. Je serais coiffé d'une tiara et j'aurais une longue robe. Toute la terre serait gentille même les criminels seraient gentils ils demanderaient la permission de voler les diamants, l'argent, les rubis et les bijoux. J'aurais une vie éternelle. Je serais tellement riche que je pourrais donner des ordinateurs à tout les élèves du monde. Mais être la reine du monde n'est pas aussi amusant que d'etre moi-même.
Ashley

Ashley Hollister , 9 ans

**Ashley Hollister, 9 ans, Lachenaie, QC
École Arc-en-ciel**

Si j'étais la reine du monde, tout le monde dépenderait sur moi. J'habiterais dans un château et j'aurais des pandas, des chattes et des chevaux. Je serais coiffée d'une tiara et j'aurais une longue robe. Toute la terre serait gentille même les criminels seraient gentils. Ils demanderaient la permission de voler les diamants, l'argent, les rubis et les bijoux. J'aurais un vie éternelle. Je serais tellement riche que je pourrais donner des ordinateurs à tous les élèves du monde. Mais être la reine du monde n'est pas aussi amusant que d'être moi-même Ashley.

If I were a Fairy Princess I would ride on a butterfly and soar through the air to my castle in a flower garden. It would be made out of smooth pebbles and flowers. I would use pink tulips for my bed. For breakfast I would have fruit. For lunch I would eat crumbs and for dinner I would have my favorite pie. I would swim and canoe in the garden's fountain. My canoe would be made out of a leaf and my paddle out of a branch. I would have a ladybug on a leash for a pet.

Erin Holloway, age 8

Erin Holloway, Age 8, Hamilton, ON
Ryckman's Corners School

If I were a fairy princess, I would ride on a butterfly, and soar through
the air to my castle in a flower garden. It would be made out of
smooth pebbles and flowers. I would use pink tulips for my bed.
For breakfast, I would have fruit. For lunch I would eat crumbs and
for dinner, I would have my favourite pie. I would swim and canoe in
the garden's fountain. My canoe would be made out of a leaf, and my
paddle out of a branch. I would have a lady bug on a leash for a pet.

If I were a potato bug, I would see the world as a dangerous place. I would be afraid of getting stepped on. If I were a cat, I would have a fenced in life. I wouldn't know what was beyond the fourth tree next to the second house. If I were a bird, I would live a free life. I would know all the sights and sounds of the world. But I'm just a kid. My life feels like a cat. My goal is to be a bird. Until I grow wings, I'll be taking flight in my dreams.

Kimberly Ivany - 12

Kimberly Ivany, Age 12, Georgetown, ON
Centennial Middle School

If I were a potato bug, I would see the world as a dangerous place.
I would be afraid of getting stepped on. If I were a cat, I would have a
fenced-in life. I wouldn't know what was beyond the fourth tree next
to the second house. If I were a bird, I would live a free life. I would
know all the sights and sounds of the world. But I'm just a kid.
My life feels like a cat. My goal is to be a bird. Until I grow wings,
I'll be taking flight in my dreams.

If I were you, I would realize that it shouldn't matter if someone is handicapped, that there's no difference between white skin and black and that it shouldn't matter if someone is rich or poor. Whether we live in Canada, Africa or Afghanistan, we should all have the right to be happy, loved, well-fed and safe. Even though we all look different, we're really the same on the inside. We all have hopes and dreams of a better life. If I were you, I would try to make our world a better place by seeing it through someone else's eyes.

Tilly Marie Jackson, age 10

Tilly Marie Jackson, Age 10, London, ON
Jeanne Sauvé French Immersion School

If I were you, I would realize that it shouldn't matter if someone is handicapped, that there's no difference between white skin and black, and that it shouldn't matter if someone is rich or poor. Whether we live in Canada, Africa, or Afghanistan, we should all have the right to be happy, loved, well-fed, and safe. Even though we all look different, we're really the same on the inside. We all have hopes and dreams of a better life. If I were you, I would try to make our world a better place by seeing it through someone else's eyes.

If I were a curious dolphin, I would race through the waves, feeling the ripples flow past my stream-lined body. I would bury my agile grey snout in the soft golden sand and come out with a tasty razor fish. I would play in the vibrant Kelp Forest amongst the seals and great whales. My thirst would call me to my mother's side, where her rich milk would replenish my energy. My powerful tail would pump me to the surface where I could breach with joy, celebrating my freedom. Then much too soon, it would be naptime.

Anna James, 10

Anna James, Age 10, Markdale, ON
Holland Chatsworth School

If I were a curious dolphin I would race through the waves feeling the ripples flow past my steamlined body. I would bury my agile grey snout in the soft golden sand and come out with a tasty razor fish. I would play in the vibrant kelp forest amongst the seals and great whales. My thirst would call me to my mother's side, where her rich milk would replenish my energy. My powerful tail would pump me to the surface where I could breach with joy, celebrating my freedom. Then much too soon it would be naptime.

Alanna Johnson, Age 9, Winnipeg, MB
St. Avila School

"If I were you, Sid, I'd be back in the tent." I turned and saw the
scariest counsellor of them all. Big Bob, who had a nasty temper.
I froze. I tried to answer, but only a tiny whisper came out. "M-me?"
"Didn't you hear me?" he boomed. I turned to run, but my legs were
pinned together. Suddenly, there was a hand on my shoulder, holding
me back, shaking me. Then, someone called, "SID!" I woke up and
saw my mother. Was I relieved! Then she said, "Big Bob is waiting to
take you to camp!" "NOOOO!"

If I were the letter "I", I'd be all-powerful. Without the letter "I", there would be no me. There would be no Ice cream, no Idiots, no Issues and not even Inventions or Ideas. Do you know what would happen if there were no Inventions or Ideas? There would be no buildings, no toilets, no stories and no politics. Enough about me, what letter would you be? Would you be "E" for Elephant or "P" for Piano? Personally, I'd be the letter "L" for Love. What other simple word can make life so interesting?

Michelle Karpman, 10

Michelle Karpman, Age 10, Montréal, QC
Roslyn School

If I were the letter 'i', I'd be all-powerful. Without the letter 'i', there would be no me. There would be no ice cream, no idiots, no issues, and not even inventions or ideas. Do you know what would happen if there were no inventions or ideas? There would be no buildings, no toilets, no stories, and no politics. Enough about me, what letter would you be? Would you be 'e' for elephant, or 'p' for piano? Personally, I'd be the letter "l" for love. What other simple word can make life so interesting?

If I were an engineer, I'd invent a new car that could go underwater. It would have air stored in the roof and the wheels would propel it through the water. It would also have wheels that could lengthen for going over slow cars on the highway instead of going around them! If you accidently go over a cliff, you push a button and out goes a parachute. Push again and you have hundreds of balloons on the bottom. They make you float! If there's only rocks at the bottom, you land on a colossal ball! Then I'd invent a plane . . .

Name: Grace Kiran Khare Age: 10

Grace Kiran Khare, Age 10, Toronto, ON
Withrow Public School

If I were an engineer, I'd invent a new car that could go underwater. It would have air stored in the roof, and the wheels would propel it through the water. It would also have wheels that could lengthen for going over slow cars on the highway, instead of going around them! If you accidentally go over a cliff, you push a button and out goes a parachute. Push again and you have hundreds of balloons on the bottom. They make you float! If there's only rocks at the bottom, you land on a colossal ball! Then I'd invent a plane......

"If I were only allowed to go through the attic door," I thought to myself as my hand inched towards the knob. There had to be an explanation for what was making that noise, and I knew I'd find it up there. "Emma" I heard my mom call. I headed downstairs, leaving the door behind me. That night as I lay in bed, all I could think about was that door. I crept out of bed and slowly climbed the attic stairs. I nervously opened the door. A box shifted! I gasped... Ahhh! Rufus you naughty little cat.

Emma Konrad, Age: 10

Emma Konrad, Age 10, Langley, BC
Topham Elementary School

"If I were only allowed to go through the attic door," I thought to myself as my hand inched toward the knob. There had to be an explanation for what was making that noise, and I knew I'd find it up there. "Emma," I heard my mom call. I headed downstairs, leaving the door behind me. That night, as I lay in bed, all I could think about was that door. I crept out of bed and climbed the attic stairs. I nervously opened the door. A box shifted! I gasped... Ahhh!! Rufus, you naughty little cat.

If I were a tree I wouldn't be any tree, I would be the Tree of Giving. If it is sunny and you are hot my leaves will provide you shade. If it is raining or cold out I will give you my warmth. If you are hungry I will share my apples. When you are thirsty I will supply you fresh water from my roots. If you need company you can sit in my branches. If you need to be loved I will hug you with my limbs. I am not only a tree I am also your friend.

Erica Kresevic 12 years old

Erica Kresevic, Age 12, Lachine, QC
Lakeside Academy

If I were a tree I wouldn't be any tree, I would be the tree of giving. If it is sunny and you are hot, my leaves will provide you shade. If it is raining or cold out, I will give you my warmth. If you are hungry, I will share my apples. When you are thirsty, I will supply you fresh water from my roots. If you need company, you can sit in my branches. If you need to be loved, I will hug you with my limbs. I am not only a tree, I am also your friend.

If I were a pen I'd be writing all day,
in a diary what my owner has to say.
On the page I'd write my owners fears,
I'd write everything from smiles to
heartbreak and tears. I hear secrets
she'd never tell. I know her thoughts,
I know them well. I know who
she loves and what she thinks
of him, his heart belongs to
someone else, but knows that
she'll win. Teardrops fall as
I zoom by, I wish I could
write, "Please don't cry," but I'm
only a pen used everyday,
when time's up, she puts
me away! :)

Patricia Krowinski, Age: 13

Patricia Krowinski, Age 13, Dundas, ON
St. Augustine School

If I were a pen, I'd be writing all day in a diary what my owner has to
say. On the page, I'd write my owner's fears. I'd write everything
from smiles to heartbreak and tears. I hear secrets she'd never tell,
I know her thoughts, I know them well. I know who she loves and
what she thinks of him, his heart belongs to someone else, but knows
that she'll win. Teardrops fall as I zoom by, I wish I could write,
"Please don't cry." But I'm only a pen, used every day. When time's
up, she puts me away.

If I were a writer I would write stories about things that can cheer people up when they are down and stories that can brighten the hearts of young children. I would write stories that would help people make the right discisions and stories that would influence them in life. I would write stories that people can relate to. I would be a writer not only for people, but for me. If I am a writer when I grow up I can share my feelings with other people in the form of a story.

Nicole Kucherenko 11

Nicole Kucherenko, Age 11, Georgetown, ON
St. Brigid School

If I were a writer, I would write stories about things that can cheer people up when they are down, and stories that would brighten the hearts of young children. I would write stories that would help people make the right decisions, and stories that would influence them in life. I would write stories that people can relate to. I would be a writer not only for people, but for me. If I am a writer when I grow up, I can share my feelings with other people in the form of a story.

If I were a musical note, I would dance merrily on the musical staff. I would sound harmonious and gleefull. Soon I would Change to an adiago beat. Then I would begin to sway mournfully filling the room with a melodious, tear-jerking tune. Gradually, the tempo would pick up speed. I would once more be allegro. The accent put on me would make me sound especially loud and forceful. I would crescendo until I would erupt into a booming fortissimo. Suddenly, without warning, I would change to a barely audible pianissimo. Then Beethoven would stand and the Audience would cheer.

Jessica Kuester, 12

Jessica Kuester, Age 12, Dixonville, AB
Dixonville School

If I were a musical note I would dance merrily on the musical staff. I would sound harmonious and gleeful. Soon I would change to an adagio beat. Then I would begin to sway mournfully filling the room with a melodious tear-jerking tune. Gradually the tempo would pick up speed. I would once more be allegro. The accent put on me would make me sound especially loud and forceful. I would cresendo until I would erupt into a booming fortissimo. Suddenly, without warning I would change to a barely audible pianissimo. Then, Beethoven would stand and the audience would cheer.

"If I were a spider, I would spin a web too."

A boy leaned against a tree trunk watching a busy spider. His yellow cat sneaked up behind him. It crouched, preparing to pounce. The boy spun around.

"Simon!" he yelled as the streak of yellow flew towards the web. The spider scurried away, but the web was broken.

"NO!" screamed the boy and chased the cat down the trail. The cat's ears were back and eyes closed to slits. It raced down the trail not knowing what it had done.

Meanwhile, the spider calmly made another web.   Benjamin Kwok, 10

Benjamin Kwok, Age 10, Victoria, BC
Hillcrest Elementary School

"If I were a spider, I would spin a web too." A boy leaned against a tree trunk watching a busy spider. His yellow cat sneaked up behind him. It crouched, preparing to pounce. The boy spun around.
"Simon!" he yelled as the streak of yellow flew towards the web. The spider scurried away, but the web was broken. "NO!" screamed the boy and chased the cat down the trail. The cat's ears were back and it's eyes closed to slits. It raced down the trail not knowing what it had done. Meanwhile the spider calmly made another web.

If I were ... spinach, I would take sugar baths so that kids could eat me without saying "Eew! Gross! It's spinach!" In Mexico, I would be salsa flavoured and in the United States I would be chocolate coated and many children would eat me. In Japan, I would taste like sushi and in China, spinach would taste like soy sauce. Flavoured spinach would make kids all around the world beg their parents to cook spinach everday. In the world there would be fewer starving children and more healthy bodies. Spinach would be a life saver!

Holly Kwok   age: 9   Ontario

Holly Kwok, Age 9, Scarborough, ON
Churchill Heights Public School

If I were spinach, I would take sugar baths so that kids could eat me without saying, "Eew! Gross! It's spinach!" In Mexico, I would be salsa-flavoured, and in the United States I would be chocolate-coated, and many children would eat me. In Japan, I would taste like sushi, and in China, spinach would taste like soy sauce. Flavoured spinach would make kids all around the world beg their parents to cook spinach every day. In the world, there would be fewer starving children and more healthy bodies. Spinach would be a life saver!

Si j'étais un génie j'irais dans le pays d'Aladin voler sur un tapis volant multicolore. J'exaucerais tous les voeux des enfants. Je serais une super héroïne. Je donnerais de l'argent aux pauvres. Je vivrais dans une lampe magique argent. Je serais d'une couleure vive. J'arrêterais la guerre, la famine dans le monde et aussi je guérirais les enfants malades. Je pourrais faire tout ce que je voudrais de mes petites mains. Ce serait vraiment, mais vraiment génial! J'èspère que je pourrais devenir un génie un de ces jours car quand je pense à toutes les choses que je pourrais faire!

Marie-Philippe Labbé 10 ans

Marie-Philippe Labbé, 10 ans, Beauport, QC
École Ste-Chrétienne

Si j'étais un génie, j'irais dans le pays d'Aladin voler sur un tapis volant multicolore. J'exaucerais tous les vœux des enfants. Je serais une super héroïne. Je donnerais de l'argent aux pauvres. Je vivrais dans une lampe magique argent. Je serais d'une couleur vive. J'arrêterais la guerre, la famine dans le monde et aussi je guérirais les enfants malades. Je pourrais faire tout ce que je voudrais de mes petites mains. Ce serait vraiment, mais vraiment génial! J'espère que je pourrais devenir un génie un de ces jours car quand je pense à toutes les choses que je pourrais faire!

If I were the boss of the Royal Canadian Mint I would have a top secret penny. It would look like any other penny except it would be bright gold, as shiney and lucky as an Olympic gold medal. There would only be one secret gold penny in all of Canada. I would send it to the stores like any plain penny. The lucky person who got it in their change when they were shopping would win a tour of The Royal Canadian Mint and a sleep over at the Prime Ministers house. Now that would be a lucky penny!

Tye Landels, age 10

Tye Landels, Age 10, Saanichton, BC
Saanichton Elementary School

If I were the boss of the Royal Canadian Mint I would have a top secret penny. It would look like any other penny except it would be bright gold, as shiny and lucky as an Olympic gold medal.
There would only be one secret gold penny in all of Canada. I would send it to the stores like any plain penny. The lucky person who got it in their change when they were shopping would win a tour of the Royal Canadian Mint and a sleep over at the Prime Minister's house. Now that would be a lucky penny!

Si j'étais une étoile, je me promènerais de
galaxie en galaxie pour illuminer les cieux;
Si j'étais le vent, j'errerrais de champs en
champs pour caresser d'une douce brise
les passants; Si j'étais une sirène, je naviguerais d'océan en océan pour faire entendre ma voix mélodieuse aux marins; Si
j'étais le feu, je brûlerais de foyer en
foyer pour réchauffer les coeurs brisés;
Si j'étais l'eau, je coulerais de ruisseau
en ruisseau pour étancher la soif de tous
les animaux; Mais voilà, je ne suis qu'une
jeune fille rêveuse aux idées surnaturelles
dans un monde bien réel.

Karine Landry, 10 ans

Karine Landry, 10 ans, Rimouski, QC
École Dominique-Savio

Si j'étais une étoile, je me promènerais de galaxie en galaxie pour illuminer les cieux; si j'étais le vent, j'errerais de champ en champ pour
caresser d'une douce brise les passants; si j'étais une sirène, je naviguerais
d'océan en océan pour faire entendre ma voix mélodieuse aux marins; si
j'étais le feu, je brûlerais de foyer en foyer pour réchauffer les cœurs
brisés; si j'étais l'eau, je coulerais de ruisseau en ruisseau pour étancher la
soif de tous les animaux; mais voilà, je ne suis qu'une jeune fille rêveuse
aux idées surnaturelles dans un monde bien réel.

*If I were a little cat,
I would wear a pretty hat!
If I were a dog, I could chase a frog!
If I were a flower, I wouldn't be a coward!
If I were a dimond ring, I would never get to sing!
If I were a bird, I would gather with a herd!
If I were a star, I would be in the sky so far!
As you can see, I am free, to be me!*

Gabrielle Langdon   7

Gabrielle Langdon, Age 7, Lethbridge, AB
Argyll Centre School

If I were a little cat, I would wear a pretty hat! If I were a dog, I could chase a frog! If I were a flower, I wouldn't be a coward! If I were a diamond ring, I would never get to sing! If I were a bird, I would gather with a herd! If I were a star, I would be in the sky so far! As you can see I'm free to be me.

If I were a bird, I would travel all around the world and sing my beautiful song. My hymn to joy and friendship and love. I would whisper through my song to rulers and commoners alike, and teach them about caring and understanding. I would try to end racism and prejudice by learning about other people's beliefs and cultures. Then teach others about what I learned. I would hope that they would then take this knowledge and come to embrace each other as a whole community. I would try and free captured souls of Evil, by singing my beautiful song.

Shannon Languay   Age → 13

Shannon Languay, Age 13, Greenfield Park, QC
St. John's School

If I were a bird, I would travel all around the world and sing my beautiful song. My hymn to joy and friendship and love. I would whisper through my song to rulers and commoners alike, and teach them about caring and understanding. I would try to end racism and prejudice by learning about other people's beliefs and cultures. Then teach others about what I learned. I would hope that they would then take this knowledge and come to embrace each other as a whole community. I would try and free captured souls of evil, by singing my beautiful song.

Si j'étais une fleur j'aurais un doux parfum comme personne ne l'aurait encore senti. Je serais une tulipe rouge avec deux feuilles vertes. Ce que je mangerais ne serait pas des hamburgers ou des frites car une fleur ne mange pas ça elle mange du produit qui se fabrique à base de: Soleil, d'eau et d'air. Tu sais, si j'étais une fleur, j'aurais besoin de racines pour aspirer l'eau et j'aurais besoin de mes feuilles pour aspirer l'air. Alors maintenant crois tu que les fleurs on la belle vie? Moi, je crois toujours qu'elles ont la belle vie!

Jennifer Laporte 9 ans

Jennifer Laporte, 9 ans, Sorel-Tracy, QC
École Ste-Anne-les-Îles

Si j'étais une fleur, j'aurais un doux parfum comme personne ne l'aurait encore senti. Je serais une tulipe rouge avec deux feuilles vertes. Ce que je mangerais ne serait pas des hamburgers ou des frites car une fleur ne mange pas ça. Elle mange du produit qui se fabrique à base de soleil, d'eau et d'air. Tu sais, si j'étais une fleur, j'aurais besoin de racines pour aspirer l'eau et j'aurais besoin de mes feuilles pour aspirer l'air. Alors maintenant crois-tu que les fleurs ont la belle vie? Moi, je crois toujours qu'elles ont la belle vie!

If I were a veterinarian I would be so happy to work with animals. I would take care of them so well. I would also make a petshop to put all the healed animals that need homes. All animals need care and love. That is why I want to be a vet. I would make a donation so that more and more people will want to adopt a pet. I will try as hard as I can to help animals and to make cures. I would love the animals a lot. It would be my dream to be a vet!

Help Animals !!

Olivia La Rue   age 10

Olivia La Rue, Age 10, Montreal, QC
Gardenview School

If I were a veterinarian I would be so happy to work with animals. I would take care of them so well. I would also make a petshop to put all the healed animals that need homes. All animals need care and love. That is why I want to be a vet. I would make a donation so that more and more people will want to adopt a pet. I will try as hard as I can to help animals and to make cures. I would love the animals a lot. It would be my dream to be a vet. Help animals!!

Si j'étais ... un ange j'irais au ciel pour aller rejoindre ma grand-mère qui est morte. Je m'amusais bien avec elle, j'allais chez elle, elle me faisais rire. Je m'ennuis d'elle, j'aimerais tant être un ange ou bien voler pour aller voir ma grand-mère pour lui dire bonjour comment ça va? Si elle aime être au paradis. Elle était belle quand elle souriait. De temps en temps je pense à elle, je rêve à elle et aussi elle m'appellait ma chouette ... Je serais contente si ma grand-mère revenais sur terre.

Paméla Lavallée 9 ans

Paméla Lavallée, 9 ans, Mercier, QC
École St-Renné

Si j'étais un ange, j'irais au ciel pour aller rejoindre ma grand-mère qui est morte. Je m'amusais bien avec elle. J'allais chez elle, elle me faisait rire. Je m'ennuie d'elle, j'aimerais tant être un ange ou bien voler pour aller voir ma grand-mère pour lui dire bonjour, comment ça va? Si elle aime être au paradis. Elle était belle quand elle souriait. De temps en temps, je pense à elle. Je rêve à elle et aussi elle m'appelait ma chouette. Je serais contente si ma grand-mère revenait sur terre.

If I were rich I would buy a mansion and have full time maids. I'd have a wonderful daughter and name her Ginger, I would buy a kitten and a puppy. I would buy a indoor pool and a hotub and a sayna. I'd buy a canopy bed for Ginger and some toys for my kitten and puppy. My butler would hire a french chef to cook my meals and my daughter would give money to the poor and I would donate money to poorer schools and. make them richer schools.
I would donate money to staples also.
I'd give money.

Janele Laws   9.

Janele Laws, Age 9, Murillo, ON
Crestview School

If I were rich, I would buy a mansion and have full-time maids.
I'd have a wonderful daughter, and name her Ginger. I would buy a
kitten and a puppy. I would buy an indoor pool, and a hot tub, and a
sauna. I'd buy a canopy bed for Ginger, and some toys for my kitten
and puppy. My butler would hire a French chef to cook my meals, and
my daughter would give money to the poor, and I would donate
money to poorer schools and make them richer schools. I would
donate money to STAPLES also. I'd give money.

Si j'étais... un papillon, je regarderais du haut du ciel, l'espace merveilleux autour de moi. Parfois, je survolerais les splendides lacs sur la terre. J'aimerais me regarder dans le lac avec mes petites ailes violettes et jaunes. Un jour, quand je descendrais comme toujours, je m'arrêterais dans un champ de fleurs. Il y aurait des reines-marguerites, des tournesols, des lilas, des jacinthes et des roses. Je rencontrerais une sauterelle qui s'appellerait Logo. Elle me montrerait d'abord sa petite maison et nous ferions davantage connaissance. Après, je la monterais sur mon dos et nous nous envolerions très haut.

Marika Lebel 10 ans

Marika Lebel, 10 ans, St-Herménégilde, QC
École Gendreau

Si j'étais un papillon, je regarderais du haut du ciel, l'espace merveilleux autour de moi. Parfois, je survolerais les splendides lacs sur la terre. J'aimerais me regarder dans le lac avec mes petites ailes violettes et jaunes. Un jour, quand je descendrais comme toujours, je m'arrêterais dans un champ de fleurs. Il y aurait des reines-marguerites, des tournesols, des lilas, des jacinthes et des roses. Je rencontrerais une sauterelle qui s'appellerait Logo. Elle me montrerait d'abord sa petite maison et nous ferions davantage connaissance. Après, je la monterais sur mon dos et nous nous envolerions très haut.

IF I were the Prime Minister of Canada, I would send food to starving children in less fortunate countries. I would try to pay off Canada's debt that grows bigger each year. I would send military supplies to our Allies in war and try to make peace with all other countries. I would try to make the people of our great nation hopes possible. I'd help the pollution by encouraging people to reduce, reuse, and recycle. Canada would hire more nurses, doctors, and teachers because health care and education are very important today. Someday, this all could come true.

michael LeBlanc, 13

Michael LeBlanc, Age 13, Cornwall, PE
East Wiltshire School

If I were the Prime Minister of Canada, I would send food to starving children in less fortunate countries. I would try to pay off Canada's debt that grows bigger each year. I would send military supplies to our allies in war, and try to make peace with all other countries. I would try to make the peoples', of our great nation, hopes possible. I'd help the pollution by encouraging people to reduce, reuse, and recycle. Canada would hire more nurses, doctors, and teachers because health care and education are very important today. Someday, this all could come true.

Si j'étais un Dieu grec, je serais Hermès. Hermès est capable de voler plus vite que le vent avec ses bottines et son casque ailé. Il est aussi le Dieu des voyageurs, des marchands, des voleurs et des médecins. Il travaille à livrer les morts en enfer. J'aimerais être Hermès pour pouvoir voyager à travers le monde gratuitement et en volant. Je donnerais alors le pouvoir à tous les médecins de soigner les gens qui souffrent et d'éliminer toutes les maladies dans le monde. Et moi je travaillerais à mener les âmes au paradis.

Thomas Léger   9 ans

Thomas Léger, 9 ans, L'Acadie, QC
École Marie Derome

Si j'étais un dieu grec, je serais Hermès. Hermès est capable de voler plus vite que le vent avec ses bottines et son casque ailé. Il est aussi le dieu des voyageurs, des marchands, des voleurs et des médecins. Il travaille à livrer les morts en enfer. J'aimerais être Hermès pour pouvoir voyager à travers le monde gratuitement et en volant. Je donnerais alors le pouvoir à tous les médecins de soigner les gens qui souffrent et d'éliminer toutes les maladies dans le monde. Et moi je travaillerais à mener les âmes au paradis.

If I were able to fly I would float with the snowflakes. Gracefully hovering over the schoolyard where children are playing in the winter. Gliding between the raindrops. Watching tulips and daffodils pop up to greet the day in Spring. Flying with the birds and the bees. Lingering with the butterflies and dragonflies on a summer afternoon. Soaring with the wind. Falling lazily with the leaves in autumn. Then the cycle starts again. Each season has a different experience to offer. I can fly when I grow up to be a pilot. For now I can only dream of flying.

Lindsey Legge   Age 10

Lindsey Legge, Age 10, Cambridge, ON
St. Gregory School

If I were able to fly, I would float with the snowflakes. Gracefully hovering over the schoolyard where children are playing in the winter. Gliding up between the raindrops, watching tulips and daffodils pop up to greet the day in spring. Flying with the birds and the bees. Lingering with the butterflies and dragonflies on a summer afternoon. Soaring with the wind. Falling lazily with the leaves in autumn. Then the cycle starts again. Each season has a different experience to offer. I can fly when I grow up to be a pilot. For now, I can only dream of flying.

Si j'étais écrivaine, j'achèterais un magnifique voilier blanc. J'irais ensuite naviguer au large, me laissant bercer par le rythme calm et apaisant de la mer enchanteresse, feuilletant inlassablement les pages encore vierges d'un carnet de bord. Je partirais à la conquête du monde, admirer les bancs de corail, m'émerveiller devant le crépuscule d'une île du pacifique et m'étendre sur les plages dorées des contrées chaleureuses du Sud. Je rentrerais ensuite à ma coquette demeure, ayant rédigé un volume intitulé L'océan. Ce livre raconterait les aventures enflamées auxquelles j'ai participé tout au long de mon épopée fantastique!

Catherine Lemay Bons

Catherine Lemay, 13 ans, St-Hyacinthe, QC
Collège St-Maurice

Si j'étais écrivaine, j'achèterais un magnifique voilier blanc. J'irais ensuite naviguer au large, me laissant bercer par le rythme calme et apaisant de la mer enchanteresse, feuilletant inlassablement les pages encores vierges d'un carnet de bord. Je partirais à la conquête du monde, admirer les bancs de corail, m'émerveiller devant le crépuscule d'une île du Pacifique et m'étendre sur les plages dorées des contrées chaleureuses du Sud. Je rentrerais ensuite à ma coquette demeure, ayant rédigé un volume intitulé L'océan. Ce livre raconterait les aventures enflammées auxquelles j'ai participé tout au long de mon épopée fantastique!

If I were to bring you to a place in my dreams, I would. But I can't. So, I shall tell you.

Step foot into an enchanting forest - so serene in its beauty, it is almost indescribable. The ground beneath your feet is cushion-soft, the trees tall and majestic. Sunlight shines through the thick, but wondrously beautiful vegetation. Then you will come to a waterfall. It's fast flowing and quiet. The rocks surrounding it are not painful; the exotic birds sing an enchanting song.

And then you realise, you've entered a realm so pure, it's only in your dreams.

Amanda Leong, 13

Amanda Leong, Age 13, Calgary, AB
ABC Charter Public School

If I were to bring you to a place in my dreams, I would, but I can't, so I shall tell you. Step foot into an enchanting forest, so serene in its beauty, it is almost indescribable. The ground beneath your feet is cushion-soft, the trees tall and majestic. Sunlight shines through the thick, but wondrously beautiful, vegetation. Then, you will come to a waterfall. It's fast-flowing and quiet. The rocks surrounding it are not painful, the exotic birds sing an enchanting song. And then you realize, you've entered a realm so pure, it's only in your dream.

If I were a fountain pen, I would be sitting in a drawer, gathering dust. I would have been passed on from generation to generation until the ball-point pens and computers came along. After the new writing instruments became popular, I would be left in a drawer and forgotten. Before, I always wrote down peoples' thoughts and feelings, but for a long time now, I have not had the opportunity to do so. I hope that in these next few years, somebody will pick me up and enable me to do what I have always enjoyed-writing.

Wansum Li   11 years

Wansum Li, Age 11, Vancouver, BC
Champlain Elementary School

If I were a fountain pen, I would be sitting in a drawer, gathering dust. I would have been passed on from generation to generation until the ballpoint pens and computers came along. After the new writing instruments became popular, I would be left in a drawer and forgotten. Before, I always wrote down people's thoughts and feelings, but for a long time now, I have not had the opportunity to do so. I hope that in these next few years, somebody will pick me up and enable me to do what I have always enjoyed -- writing.

If I were a red ant I'd climb onto a dandelion plant. The wind might rise and blow me away and I'd land on the neighbour's dog. I would bite his ear and he would run around in a "furry" frenzy. I'd be launched off and land on a car. It would take me to a far away place. Then I would get a strange band of ants to help me dig my way back home. It would take a very long time, but I know I would get there. Even if ants are tiny they never give up.

Nathan MacInnes 11

Nathan MacInnes, Age 11, Morin-Heights, QC
Home-schooled

If I were a red ant, I'd climb onto a dandelion plant. The wind might rise and blow me away, and I'd land on the neighbour's dog. I would bite his ear, and he would run around in a 'furry' frenzy. I'd be launched off and land on a car. It would take me to a faraway place. Then I would get a strange band of ants to help me dig my way back home. It would take a very long time, but I know I would get there. Even if ants are tiny, they never give up.

If I were a loonie, my life would not be bland, cause every day; i'd pass from hand to hand. Sunday i'm an offering from you to your church. Monday i'm the G.S.T. on that 'gotta have it' shirt. Tuesday i'm the tip on a table, along with two dollars more. Wednesday i'm in the pinball machine ... you've got the highest score!! Thursday, I bought some ice cream on that hot summer day. Friday; a can of coke... now you're on your way. Saturday, we do nothing much, cause you rented a movie called 'Blue Crush'...

... If I were a toonie...

Michelle L. Mackenzie - 13 years old

Michelle L. MacKenzie, Age 13, Calgary, AB
St. Paul's Academy

If I were a loonie, my life would not be bland,
cause every day I'd pass from hand to hand.
Sunday, I'm an offering from you to your church.
Monday, I'm the G.S.T. on that 'gotta have it' shirt.
Tuesday, I'm the tip on a table along with two dollars more. Wednesday, I'm in the pinball machine ... you've got the highest score!! Thursday, I bought some ice cream, on that hot summer day. Friday, a can of coke ... now you're on your way. Saturday, we do nothing much 'cause you rented the movie, 'Blue Crush'... If I were a toonie...

Si j'étais une plume, de l'encre j'utiliserais pour glisser entre les doigts de celui qu'on appellerait le poète. Si j'étais une plume... goutte par goutte je me laisserais tremper dans l'encre magique pour qu'il puisse faire chanter les mots et les faire danser sur vos lèvres. Avec mon poète, je voyagerais et j'irais droit au cœur écrire les plus beaux mots du monde! Si j'étais une plume... petite coquine je suis, j'irais vous chatouiller le bout du nez pour vous montrer que même délicate et enjouée, je peux vous emballer avec les mots que j'écris. Ah! Si j'étais une plume...

Lori-Ann MacLellan 12 ans

Lori-Ann MacLellan, 12 ans, Vaudreuil-Dorion, QC
École Lionel Groulx

Si j'étais une plume, de l'encre j'utiliserais pour glisser entre les doigts de celui qu'on appellerait le poète. Si j'étais une plume... goutte par goutte je me laisserais tremper dans l'encre magique pour qu'il puisse faire chanter les mots et les faire danser sur vos lèvres. Avec mon poète, je voyagerais et j'irais droit au cœur écrire les plus beaux mots du monde! Si j'étais une plume... petite coquine je suis, j'irais vous chatouiller le bout du nez pour vous montrer que même délicate et enjouée, je peux vous emballer avec les mots que j'écris. Ah! Si j'étais une plume...

If I were not my parents' son, I would jump for joy. I would be free to roam where I wish. I would be at liberty to do what I wish when I please. Whether or not to do my homework would be my choice. The drudgery of piano lessons would not be an issue. Manners and respect for others would be non-existent.

Alas, it's only a dream. I am constrained to behave appropriately, mind my manners, do my homework, be cultured, responsible, and respect everyone and everything around me. If I weren't my parents' son, I wouldn't exist.

Arif Mahboob   10

Arif Mahboob, Age 10, Pickering, ON
Frenchman's Bay Public School

If I were not my parents' son, I would jump for joy. I would be free to roam where I wish. I would be at liberty to do what I wish when I please. Whether or not to do my homework would be my choice. The drudgery of piano lessons would not be an issue. Manners and respect for others would be non-existent. Alas, it's only a dream. I am constrained to behave appropriately, mind my manners, do my homework, be cultured, responsible, and respect everyone and everything around me. If I weren't my parents' son, I wouldn't exist.

If I were a brave Knight, I would storm off into a fight. Onto the battlefield we go, with no intention to yield or be slow.

The sun sets, and some lie at rest. The battle is done, and we have won! But we are sorrowful to say, that some of our friends have gone away.

The king is proud and at rest, and invites a crowd because we have done our best. Night comes and we fall fast asleep, hoping that our bravery will Keep.

Rachel Mahon   Age 12.

Rachel Mahon, Age 12, Toronto, ON
Home-schooled

If I were a brave knight, I would storm off into a fight. Onto the battlefield we go, with no intention to yield or be slow. The sun sets and some lie at rest. The battle is done, and we have won! But we are sorrowful to say, that some of our friends have gone away. The King is proud and at rest, and invites a crowd because we have done our best. Night comes and we fall fast asleep, hoping that our bravery will keep.

If I were the sun, I'd be the light of love and hate. If I were the moon, I'd be the darkness of pain and anger. If I were the stars, I'd be the twinkle of sadness and joy. If I were music, I'd be the notes of excitement and anxiety. If I were colour, I'd be the prism of patience and hope. If I were fire, I'd be the warmth of good and bad. But best of all, I AM all of these. Each and every human is, too. Just look deep into yourself and you will find it.

Carmen Mak, 13

Carmen Mak, Age 13, Vancouver, BC
Eric Hamber Secondary School

If I were the sun, I'd be the light of love and hate. If I were the moon, I'd be the darkness of pain and anger. If I were the stars, I'd be the twinkle of sadness and joy. If I were music, I'd be the notes of excitement and anxiety. If I were colour, I'd be the prism of patience and hope. If I were fire I'd be the warmth of good and bad. But best of all, I am all of these. Each and every human is, too. Just look deep into yourself and you will find it.

Si J'étais...un mouton je sauterais dans les rêve.Moi je ferais rêver les enfants.Mon nom serais Frisou ou Cafou.J'aurais les pattes noirs et la laine blanche.Un mouton aussi Sage mérite une famille.Je n'aimerais pas me faire tondre.Je m'amuserais avec mes amies les chèvres et je bondirais dans les champs de fleur.Je mangerais de belle fleur rouge bleu jaune et des feuille verte.Je souhaiterais habiter dans une charmante et petite ferme avec des poules des chatons des vache et des chevaux mais je ne toucherais pas le gros méchant taureau pas très gentil.

Sarah Manseau   9 ans

Sarah Manseau, 9 ans, Nicolet, QC
École Arc-en-ciel

Si j'étais un mouton, je sauterais dans les rêves. Moi, je ferais rêver les enfants. Mon nom serait Frisou ou Cafou. J'aurais les pattes noires et la laine blanche. Un mouton aussi sage mérite une famille. Je n'aimerais pas me faire tondre. Je m'amuserais avec mes amies les chèvres et je bondirais dans les champs de fleurs. Je mangerais de belles fleurs rouges, bleues, jaunes et des feuilles vertes. Je souhaiterais habiter dans une charmante petite ferme avec des poules, des chatons, des vaches et des chevaux, mais je ne toucherais pas le gros méchant taureau pas très gentil.

If I wera a flower,
I would grow in the grass in
the backyard or a garden
or the front yard.
I would like to be a
purple rose. I would grow
by the sun and by people
watering me with the
green hose or watering
can or rain water.
No one would pick me
or touch me, just look
at me. Do you know
what colour my leaves
would be? They would
grow green and sometimes
red. I would be warm in
the sun.
              Katrina Marshall, 4

Katrina Marshall, Age 4, Kingston, ON
Home-schooled

If I were a flower, I would grow in the grass in the backyard or
a garden or the front yard. I would like to be a purple rose. I would
grow by the sun and by people watering me with the green hose or
watering can or rain water. No one would pick me or touch me, just
look at me. Do you know what colour my leaves would be? They
would grow green and sometimes red. I would be warm in the sun.

If I were a furgle from the
fabled realm of Nark, I'd
build myself a cozy of thornberry tree bark. My wondrously
comfy nest would be positioned
on a ledge, I'd be so very
careful not to fall over the
edge. Furgles are quite ambitious
you surely soon will see, for
in my homely nest I'd host
my company. A gathering of
friends would be a dangerous affair, while sitting in
a lofty perch ten miles in the
air. All things considered I
bring the truth to you, I'm
glad I'm not a furgle, I think
you should be too.
Robert Mason   13

Robert Mason, Age 13, St. Catharines, ON
Sheridan Park School

If I were a furgle from the fabled realm of Nark, I'd build a cozy nest of thornberry tree bark. My wondrously comfy nest would be positioned on a ledge, I'd be so very careful not to fall over the edge. Furgles are quite ambitious, you surely soon will see, for in my homey nest, I'd host my company. A gathering of friends would be a danger-ous affair, while sitting in a lofty perch ten miles in the air. All things considered, I bring the truth to you, I'm glad I'm not a furgle, I think you should be too.

If I were a picture frame, I would want
to surround the picture of Mona Lisa.
It's a very famous painting. I would be so
happy and show myself off. I would travel
around the world so much with Leonardo
DaVinci's painting. I would be gold & silver.
Everybody would be so excited over the
Picture of Mona Lisa and me. I would be
In a very important museum in Europe.
(and maybe America). But, when I get old,
they would replace me with a different
Frame. But, at least I would have a long,
very exciting life! The End!

Kara-Leigh Ann Matiaszow, 8

Kara-Leigh Ann Matiaszow, Age 8, Andrew, AB
Andrew School

If I were a picture frame, I would want to surround the picture of
Mona Lisa. It's a very famous painting. I would be so happy and
show myself off. I would travel around the world so much with
Leonardo da Vinci's painting. I would be gold and silver. Everybody
would be so excited over the picture of Mona Lisa and me. I would
be in every important museum in Europe (and maybe America).
But when I get old, they would replace me with a different picture
frame. But at least I would have a long, very exciting life!
THE END!

If I were in control of the earth, of this planet, I would make a difference. If I had power, I would make changes. I would make sure this beautiful planet was preserved for my generation, elder generations and those of the future. I would create laws to protect animals, plants, humans, and nature. I would enforce peace, love and friendship. Though sometimes peace is a difficult goal to attain. I would make sure all children had an education, a home, food and a loving family. If I were to change the world.

Tessie Mazi, 13

Tessie Mazi, Age 13, Niagara Falls, ON
Our Lady of Mount Carmel School

If I were in control of the Earth, of this planet, I would make a difference. If I had power, I would make changes. I would make sure this beautiful planet was preserved for my generation, elder generations and those of the future. I would create laws to protect animals, plants, humans, and nature. I would enforce peace, love and friendship. Though sometimes peace is a difficult goal to attain I would make sure all children had an education, a home, food and a loving family. If I were to change the world.

If I were a computer virus, I'd travel through the internet at the speed of light, looking for a computer to infect, I sighed as I dodged a Norton Anti virus system. Just as I finished my phrase, an e-mail swept me through a portal that said, " Government Computer!" "Yeah!! My wish came true." I hollered as I went into a mad dash toward the motherboard! As I swam in the data streams, I noticed that I was on a direct course for a firewall! I tried to swim back but the current was too strong. I was obliterated.

Evan McKenzie   11

Evan McKenzie, Age 11, Edmonton, AB
St. James School

If I were a computer virus, I'd travel through the Internet at the speed of light, looking for a computer to infect. I sighed as I dodged a Norton Anti-Virus system. Just as I finished my phrase, an email swept me through a portal that said, 'Government Computer'. "YEAH!! My wish came true!!" I hollered as I went into a mad dash toward the motherboard! As I swam in the data streams, I noticed that I was on a direct course for a firewall! I tried to swim back but the current was too strong. I was obliterated.

If I were ...   oct 21, 2002

If I were the wind I would sore
thraugh the villiages, trees and look at
all the people.
I would make sure everyone stayed nice
and cool, through out the hot summer
days.
Also I would get the biggest clouds
in the world and bring them to earth and let
everyone ride the   clouds high in
the sky.
The wind would tickle the faces of young children.
But I would make the waves everywhere grow so
nice and big for everyone at the beach.
If I where the wind I would fill the world
with joy, laughter, smiles and peace.

                by: Kylie Ann McKibbon!! Age 11

Kylie Ann McKibbon, Age 11, Sudbury, ON
Queen Elizabeth II Public School

If I were the wind, I would soar through the villages,
trees, and look at all the people. I would make sure
everyone stayed nice and cool, throughout the hot
summer days. Also, I would get the biggest clouds in
the world, and bring them to earth, and let everyone ride the clouds
high in the sky. The wind would tickle the faces of young children.
But I would make the waves everywhere grow nice and big for everyone at the beach. If I were the wind, my smile would fill the world
with joy, laughter, smiles and peace.

Si j'étais un oiseau, je ferais le tour du monde. En chemin, je laisserais tomber une poudre magique. Cette poudre permetterait au gens de réaliser tous leurs souhaits. Je laisserais aussi tomber mes plumes avec une couleur différente pour chaque pays. Celle-ci arrêterait la guerre, la haine, la violence, et la pollution. Quand je ferais le tour du monde, tous les gens seraient éblouis par mes multiples couleurs. Ils arrêteraient ainsi de chasser les animaux pour le plaisir. À la fin de mon voyage, j'aurais combattu la misère pour que tous puissent être heureux dans ce qu'ils veulent être.

Emy. P. Ménard   11 ans

Emy P. Ménard, 11 ans, Granby, QC
École St-Luc

Si j'étais un oiseau, je ferais le tour du monde. En chemin, je laisserais tomber une poudre magique. Cette poudre permettrait aux gens de réaliser tous leurs souhaits. Je laisserais aussi tomber mes plumes avec une couleur différente pour chaque pays. Celles-ci arrêteraient la guerre, la haine, la violence et la pollution. Quand je ferais le tour du monde, tous les gens seraient éblouis par mes multiples couleurs. Ils arrêteraient ainsi de chasser les animaux pour le plaisir. À la fin de mon voyage, j'aurais combattu la misère pour que tous puissent être heureux dans ce qu'ils veulent être.

If I were that girl that was terrified at Halloween while she was trick or treating, I wouldn't be able to sleep at night. This is how she said the story went: "I was walking down the street with my friend on Halloween night and saw a dark, old, scary house. I rang on the door-bell, the door opened by it self and their were no lights on. I put my flash-light on and I looked at my friend and then beside her was a ghost! sense that day I never went trick or treating again".

Chantel Mikhael, 11 years old.

Chantel Mikhael, Age 11, Toronto, ON
St-Charles Garnier School

If I were that girl who was terrified at Halloween while she was trick-or-treating, I wouldn't be able to sleep at night. This is how she said the story went: "I was walking down the street with my friend on Halloween night, and saw a dark, old, scary house. I rang the doorbell. The door opened by itself and there were no lights on. I put my flashlight on and I looked at my friend and then beside her was a ghost! Since that day, I've never gone trick-or-treating again."

If I were the Sun, I would lovingly watch over my nine children. Each morning I would greet them with a warm smile and a big hug. Before they'd go to school I would make sure Saturn didn't forget her rings, Pluto was dressed warm, and Jupiter looked after Mercury. I would remind Uranus and Neptune not to fight, Mars to wear sunscreen and I would tell Venus to not let the boys kiss her. I would tell Earth that I love her very much because the child with the biggest problems needs the *most* love and attention.

Julia Miskey, age 10

Julia Miskey, Age 10, Barrie, ON
École la Source

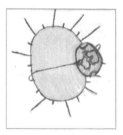

If I were the sun, I would lovingly watch over my nine children. Each morning, I would greet them with a warm smile and a big hug. Before they'd go to school, I would make sure Saturn didn't forget her rings, Pluto was dressed warm, and Jupiter looked after Mercury. I would remind Uranus and Neptune not to fight, Mars to wear sunscreen, and I would tell Venus to not let the boys kiss her. I would tell Earth that I love her very much because the child with the biggest problems needs the most love and attention.

If I were a monkey I would live with my mom and dad. I also love bananas they are the thing I eat. I live with a whole lot of monkeys like my Aunt and Uncle. One time I couldn't find them. When I was about to go home I found out that I was lost, so I made the loudest monkey sound I could make and before I could blink my mom and dad were there. Then we went to Staples and bought the best stuff for monkey school.

Chantal Mitchell 9

Chantal Mitchell, Age 9, Prince George, BC
Austin Road Elementary School

If I were a monkey, I would live with my mom and dad. I also love bananas, they are the thing I eat. I live with a whole lot of monkeys, like my aunt and uncle. One time I went off to play, to look for my cousins. I couldn't find them. When I was about to go home, I found out that I was lost, so I made the loudest monkey sound I could make and, before I could blink, my mom and dad were here. Then we went to STAPLES and bought the best stuff for monkey school.

If I were a pencil, I'd have to be sharpened 100 times every day. Some kids would break me in half and bite me like a beaver would. Then I would be scraped with scissors. Sometimes I'm thrown in the garbage. Some people play-toss-the-pencil game. But no one cares that I'm a pencil, And I don't like it! Now there is my enemy-the Eraser. If I do Art he Erases my precious work! Sometimes I wish I was Something interesting, But Sometimes I like being a pencil, It's cool! Yeah!

by: SAFA MOHAMMED AGE: 11

Safa Mohammed, Age 11, Brampton, ON
Williams Parkway Public School

If I were a pencil I'd have to be sharpened 100 times every day. Some kids would break me in half, and bite me like a beaver would. Then I would be scraped with scissors. Sometimes I'm also thrown in the garbage. Some people throw me and play toss-the-pencil game. But no one cares if I'm a pencil, and I don't like it! Now there's my enemy. The Eraser. If I do art he erases my precious work! I wish I could be something interesting, but sometimes being a pencil is cool! Yeah!

Si j'étais un oiseau je ne voudrais pas vivre dans un zoo. J'irais avec ma famille à la chasse aux chenilles. Je ferais des petites bêtises en mangeant des friandises. Je planerais dans les airs pour braver le tonnerre. Mes ailes brunes s'envoleraient vers la lune. Je m'appellerais Charlotte et je serais amie avec les marmottes. Avec mes amies je jouerais au "Monopoly". Je m'achèterais des bracelets qui sentirais le muguet. J'irais à l'école avec ma petite boussole. L'école ne durerais que 50 minutes juste le temps d'y atterir en parachute.

Charlotte Morais 10 ans

Charlotte Morais, 10 ans, Montréal, QC
École St-Paul-de-la-Croix

Si j'étais un oiseau, je ne voudrais pas vivre dans un zoo. J'irais avec ma famille à la chasse aux chenilles. Je ferais des petites bêtises en mangeant des friandises. Je planerais dans les airs pour braver le tonnerre. Mes ailes brunes s'envoleraient vers la lune. Je m'appellerais Charlotte et je serais amie avec les marmottes. Avec mes amies, je jouerais au « Monopoly ». Je m'achèterais des bracelets qui sentiraient le muguet. J'irais à l'école avec ma petite boussole. L'école ne dure-erait que 50 minutes juste le temps d'y atterrir en parachute.

Si j'étais le soleil, lorsque viendrait l'hiver j'essaierais d'envoyer mes rayons les plus chauds pour réchauffer ceux qui ont froid. Puis lorsque l'été remplacerait l'hiver, je demanderais à mon ami le vent de souffler un peu pour les pauvres gens qui ont chaud. Cependant, j'essaierais moi-même de me dissimuler derrière les nuages, mes compagnons, de temps en temps, pour ne pas trop déranger la population avec mes rayons très puissants. Au moment où il serait temps pour moi de me coucher, je lancerais quelques derniers faisceaux de chaleur afin d'être sûr de rejoindre tous les cœurs pour un avenir meilleur.

Claudya Morin 12 ans

Claudya Morin, 12 ans, Laval, QC
École Regina Assumpta

Si j'étais le soleil, lorsque viendrait l'hiver j'essaierais d'envoyer mes rayons les plus chauds pour réchauffer ceux qui ont froid. Puis, lorsque l'été remplacerait l'hiver, je demanderais à mon ami le vent de souffler un peu pour les pauvres gens qui ont chaud. Cependant, j'essaierais moi-même de me dissimuler derrière les nuages, mes compagnons de temps en temps, pour ne pas trop déranger la population avec mes rayons très puissants. Au moment où il serait temps pour moi de me coucher, je lancerais quelques derniers faisceaux de chaleur afin d'être sûr de rejoindre tous les cœurs pour un avenir meilleur.

"If I were"... said Henry the elephant. "If you were what?" asked his friend Zoolu. Zoolu is a monkey. Henry and Zoolu live up on top of the clouds, in Magical Lollipop Land. They were walking along Sugar Plum Lane. Henry was about to continue his sentence when suddenly, Zoolu was Kidnapped by the Evil Bubble Gum King. "Help me!" screamed Zoolu. Henry had an idea. He took a piece of Bubble Gum and blew a huge bubble. He threw the bubble and trapped the King in it. "You're a hero" said Zoolu. "If I were a hero" whispered Henry.

Cassondra Morrissey, 12

Cassondra Morrissey, Age 12, Burlington, ON
Pineland Public School

"If I were..." said Henry the elephant. "If you were what?" asked his friend Zoolu. Zoolu is a monkey. Henry and Zoolu live up on top of the clouds, in Magical Lollipop Land. They were walking along Sugar Plum Lane. Henry was about to continue his sentence when, suddenly, Zoolu was kidnapped by the evil Bubble Gum King. "Help me!" screamed Zoolu. Henry had an idea. He took a piece of bubble gum and blew a huge bubble. He threw the bubble and trapped the king in it. "You're a hero," said Zoolu. "If I were a hero," whispered Henry...

Robert Motum, 10

Robert Motum, Age 10, Oshawa, ON
Harmony Heights Public School

If I were a Canadian flag, I would soar proudly above many interesting places. In Ottawa, I would feel very important representing my country on top of the Parliament Buildings. I would weep at Remembrance Day ceremonies with the war veterans. At hockey games, I would cheer Canada on. With Canadian soldiers overseas, I would stand helpful and strong on peacekeeping missions. If I had my choice, I'd like to be the flag at my school. It is raised every day by grade six students like me. It stands happily over our safe and fun school.

If I were a butterfly I would want to be the most beautiful butterfly with colors of red, orange, yellow, green, blue, and purple, lik a rainbow. If I were a butterfly, I could fly high and low. I could play sky tag and hide and seek with the other butterflies. At nightfall I would fly home and then in the morning I would wake up and eat a breakfast of necktar. After breakfast I would fly into the sky and through the clouds. A butterfly is the only thing I'd want to be besides being me!

Olivia Mroczek age 10

Olivia Mroczek, Age 10, Edmonton, AB
St. Gerard Catholic School

If I were a butterfly, I would want to be the most beautiful butterfly, with colours of red, orange, yellow, green, blue and purple, like a rainbow. If I were a butterfly, I could fly high and low. I could play sky tag and hide and seek with the other butterflies. At nightfall, I would fly home and then, in the morning, I would wake up and eat a breakfast of nectar. After breakfast, I would fly into the sky and through the clouds. A butterfly is the only thing I'd want to be besides being me!

If I were the overblown, white clouds in the sky, I would sprinkle light droplets of rain that tingles people's faces during spring. Throughout summer, when the blazing sun grills the earth, I would create a solar eclipse until the climate becomes temperate again. Once autumn approaches, I would leave on vacation so the world would light up with warmth before the frosty winter comes. When winter arrives, I would snow for weeks so the snow "sculptures" would be seven hundred centimetres elevated! I would never feel lonely since new clouds would be evaporated from water, creating more friends everyday!

Mei Chi Ng   Age 11

Mei Chi Ng, Age 11, Delta, BC
Pinewood Elementary School

If I were the overblown white clouds in the sky, I would sprinkle light droplets of rain that tingle people's faces during spring. Throughout summer, when the blazing sun grills the earth, I would create a solar eclipse until the climate becomes temperate again. Once autumn approaches, I would leave on vacation so the world would light up with warmth before the frosty winter comes. When winter arrives, I would snow for weeks so the snow 'sculptures' would be seven hundred centimetres elevated! I would never feel lonely, since new clouds would be evaporated from water, creating more friends every day.

If I were trapped upstairs in a flaming house, with a baby, a cat and a dog, I'd jump over the flaming chair. After dodging past the falling cabinet, I would grab the cat. At the door to the baby's room, I'd face flames with a bucket of water, grab the baby, then crawl away. I'd race down the stairs, and catch the dog as he is about to be encircled by flames. With the cat and dog in one hand, and the baby in the other, I'd sprint outside to safety. Fortunately, I'm not caught in a flaming building!

Emma Jane Nicholson, 13

Emma Jane Nicholson, Age 13, Sarnia, ON
Cathcart Boulevard School

If I were trapped upstairs in a flaming house with a baby, a cat, and a dog, I'd jump over the flaming chair. After dodging past the falling cabinet, I would grab the cat. At the door to the baby's room, I'd face flames with a bucket of water, grab the baby, then crawl away. I'd race down the stairs, and catch the dog as he is about to be encircled by flames. With the cat and dog in one hand, and the baby in the other, I'd sprint outside to safety. Fortunately, I'm not caught in a flaming building.

If I were needing inspiration I'd think of Meg. Meg has been my friend for fourteen years. Six years ago she was diagnosed with a heart condition and was supposed to die. The diagnosis was wrong because Meg has determination to live. It is eight years later and Meg is still with us. She faces challenges such as arthritis, an enlarged heart, diabetes and now blindness. My friend never complains but adapts to challenges. Meg has learned to use her sense of smell to guide her. She teaches me. She is ninety-eight in human years, my incredible dog, Meg.

Baylee North Age: 11

Baylee North, Age 11, Chatham, ON
Tecumseh Public School

If I were needing inspiration I'd think of Meg. Meg has been my friend for fourteen years. Six years ago she was diagnosed with a heart condition and was supposed to die. The diagnosis was wrong because Meg has determination to live. It is eight years later and Meg is still with us. She faces challenges such as arthritis, an enlarged heart, diabetes, and now blindness. My friend never complains but adapts to challenges. Meg has learned to use her sense of smell to guide her. She teaches me. She is ninety-eight in human years, my incredible dog, Meg.

If I were a tree I would be a home to small animals. The cool autumn breeze would shuffle through my red and yellow leaves. The earth would be like covers warming up my roots. At night I would watch the bright stars as they would shine through my branches. In the morning I would watch the beautiful sun rise and bring light to the world. When rain would fall down from the sky it would be like a buffet of food to my roots. It would be nice to be a tree but I rather be me.

Carolina Nowak Campos ☺ ♡ 9

Carolina Nowak Campos, Age 9, Mississauga, ON
St. Raymond Catholic School

If I were a tree, I would be a home to small animals. The cool autumn breeze would shuffle through my red and yellow leaves. The earth would be like covers warming up my roots. At night, I would watch the bright stars as they would shine through my branches. In the morning, I would watch the beautiful sun rise and bring light to the world. When rain would fall down from the sky, it would be like a buffet of food to my roots. It would be nice to be a tree, but I'd rather be me.

If I were a geni, and I could not be free unless my master wished for it, I would change the rules a little. I would tell them that I would grant them two wishes if they promised that on the third wish, they would wish for my freedom. If my master was dishonest, and used the last wish for something else, after granting it, (since I was a slave to my master) I would take it back (because after the third wish, I would not have to obey them). My former master would be powerless to stop me, and I could find someone more trustworthy to be my new master.

- Claire Odecki, age 12.

Claire Odecki, Age 12, Gloucester, ON
St. Mark's School

If I were a genie, and I could not be free unless my master wished for it, I would change the rules a little. I would tell them that they I would grant them two wishes if they promised that on the third wish, they would wish for my freedom. If my master was dishonest, and used the last wish for something else, after granting it (since I was a slave to my master), I would take it back (because after the third wish, I would not have to obey them). My former master would be powerless to stop me, and I could find someone more trustworthy to be my new master.

Si J'étais...Un orang-outang je sauterais de branche en branche pour Atteindre la cîme des arbres pour y Appercevoir les magnifiques Couchers de soleil. J'y verrais toutes sortes de couleurs eblouissantes Comme rouge flamboyant, orange éclatant et un merveilleux jaune orangé. Le matin je me léverais très tôt pour voir le lever du Soleil. Je dégusterais plein de beaux fruits exotiques qui rendraient mon poils d'un brun roux extraordinaire. Ensuite j'irais rejoindre ma famille qui m'attend avec impatience pour Commencer un delicieux repas de noix de coco.

Mathilde Ouellet   10 ans

Mathilde Ouellet, 10 ans, Chicoutimi, QC
École St-Denis

Si j'étais un orang-outang, je sauterais de branche en branche pour atteindre la cîme des arbres, pour y apercevoir les magnifiques couchers de soleil. J'y verrais toutes sortes de couleurs éblouissantes comme rouge flamboyant, orange éclatant et un merveilleux jaune orangé. Le matin, je me lèverais très tôt pour voir le lever du soleil. Je dégusterais plein de beaux fruits exotiques qui rendraient mon poil d'un brun roux extraordinaire. Ensuite, j'irais rejoindre ma famille qui m'attend avec impatience pour commencer un délicieux repas de noix de coco.

If I were a pink rose, I would be at a flower boutique. One day I would be sitting in my beautiful wrapping, when a young gentleman would come in asking for one pink rose! So, the sales lady came over and picked me up. Then, the gentleman paid for me and took me home. Next, the gentleman would take me out. A young lady would answer the door and would be given the pink rose. So, if I were a rose, I would be a sign of true love. Also, I would be a present for a loved one.

Adelina Palermo   Age 11

Adelina Palermo, Age 11, Toronto, ON
St. Eugene Catholic School

If I were a pink rose, I would be at a flower boutique. One day I would be sitting in my beautiful wrapping, when a young gentleman would come in asking for one pink rose! So, the sales lady came over and picked me up. Then, the gentleman payed for me and took me home. Next the gentleman would take me out. A young lady would answer the door and would be given the pink rose. So, if I were a rose, I would be a sign of true love. Also, I would be a present for a loved one.

If I were a cigarette, I would slid
out of my box into a girls hand. There
would be a washed out girl staring down
at me, frightened. She would be pale and
bony. She would have cinnemon brown hair and
a white cardigan dropping over her shoulders.
I hear voices above me. A group of girls
would bribe this frightened girl to smoke
me. She pauses, looks at me and back
at the girls. This washed out girl smilies
at this point and looks at the mean
groups and walks away.

Kelsey Paquin, age 13

Kelsey Paquin, Age 13, Regina, SK
Douglas Park Public School

If I were a cigarette, I would slide out of my box into a girl's hand.
There would be a washed out girl staring down at me, frightened.
She would be pale and bony. She would have cinnamon brown hair
and a white cardigan dropping over her shoulders. I hear voices above
me. A group of girls would bribe this frightened girl to smoke me.
She pauses, looks at me and back at the girls. This washed out girl
smiles at this point and looks at the mean group and walks away.

If I were a warrior marching off to war I would bring along a shield of the finest metal, use a bow of supple smooth yew, and bring along a sword of the finest tempered steel. for armor I would wear chain mail covered by tempered steel plates. My helmet would be heavily infused with steel and have slits for the eyes and mouth. To ride into battle I would take the most gallant of steeds, a spirited charger from the King's own regiment. In battle I would be skilful and courageous. If I were a warrior...

Lewis Peacock   age 13

Lewis Peacock, Age 13, Toronto, ON
Bowmore Public School

If I were a warrior marching off to war, I would bring along a shield of the finest metal, use a bow of supple smooth yew, and bring along a sword of the finest tempered steel. For armour I would wear chain mail covered by tempered steel plates. My helmet would be heavily infused with steel and have slits for the eyes and mouth. To ride into battle I would take the most gallant of steeds, a spirited charger from the King's own regiment. In battle I would be skillful and courageous. If I were a warrior…

Si j'étais entomologiste je traverserais le monde à la recherche d'insectes et d'anthropodes. J'irais des déserts les plus arides aux forêts tropicales pour en capturer. Le premier pays que je visiterais serais Madagascar car je pense que cette île d'Afrique couvre une grande diversité d'insectes rares et peut-être même uniques. J'aurais mon insectarium avec plusieurs spécimens de tailles différentes et de toutes sortes de couleurs magnifiques. Je fabriquerais plusieurs sortes de pièges différents pour attraper plusieurs espèces d'insectes variées et pour avoir la plus grosse collection du monde. J'ai maintenant dit ce que j'aimerais faire plus tard. Enfin j'espère

Antoine Archambault 10 ans

Antoine Archambault, 10 ans, Terrebonne, QC
École Notre-Dame

Si j'étais entomologiste, je traverserais le monde à la recherche d'insectes et d'anthropodes. J'irais des déserts les plus arides aux forêts tropicales pour en capturer. Le premier pays que je visiterais serait Madagascar car je pense que cette île d'Afrique couvre une grande diversité d'insectes rares et peut-être même uniques. J'aurais mon insectarium avec plusieurs spécimens de tailles différentes et de toutes sortes de couleurs magnifiques. Je fabriquerais plusieurs sortes de pièges différents pour attraper plusieurs espèces d'insectes variées et pour avoir la plus grosse collection du monde. J'ai maintenant dit ce que j'aimerais faire plus tard. Enfin j'espère!

If I were prettier, people would smile upon me. If I were smarter, people would ask my opinion. If I were stronger, people would admire me. If I were braver, people would cheer for me. If you and I did not try to look like a magazine picture, we would be prettier. If we did not try to act like somebody else, we would be smarter. If we did not worry about what others thought, we would be stronger. If we did what we choose, we would be braver. If we were ourselves, we would be much happier.

Monica Petek, 11

Monica Petek, Age 11, Regina, SK
St. Matthew School

If I were prettier, people would smile upon me. If I were smarter, people would ask my opinion. If I were stronger, people would admire me. If I were braver, people would cheer for me. If you and I did not try to look like a magazine picture, we would be prettier. If we did not try to act like somebody else, we would be smarter. If we did not worry about what others thought, we would be stronger. If we did what we chose, we would be braver. If we were ourselves, we would be much happier.

Si j'étais... un livre j'aurais un couvercle vert forêt avec des desins or dessus. Je changerais de style selon l'humeur du lecteur. Des fois, je serais un livre de blagues, parfois un romon d'aventure, même un livre de mots croisés et plusieurs autres genres. Je m'assurerais que ceux qui me possèdent soient en harmonie avec tout le monde. Je pourais convaincre le monde que la guerre est inutile et que la vengeance ne cause que des problèmes personne n'aurart besoin d'acheter des millions de livres, parce que je me renouvellerais sans cesse. Je pourrais vraiment changer le monde!

Carole-Ann Picard, 12 ans

Carole-Ann Picard, 12 ans, Port-Cartier, QC
École Riverview

Si j'étais un livre, j'aurais un couvercle vert forêt avec des dessins or dessus. Je changerais de style selon l'humeur du lecteur. Des fois, je serais un livre de blagues, parfois un roman d'aventures, même un livre de mots croisés et plusieurs autres genres. Je m'assurerais que ceux qui me possèdent soient en harmonie avec tout le monde. Je pourrais convaincre le monde que la guerre est inutile et que la vengeance ne cause que des problèmes. Personne n'aurait besoin d'acheter des millions de livres, parce que je me renouvellerais sans cesse. Je pourrais vraiment changer le monde!

Si j'étais une maman, je travaillerais fort pour mes enfants. Je les surveillerais comme la prunelle de mes yeux parce que mes enfants ce serait ce qu'il y aurait de plus précieux. J'apprendrais à mes enfants à être polis et respectueux tout en suivant les règles de la maison. Je les prénommerais Caroline et Jean-Philippe. Caroline serait une petite fille travaillante et Jean-Philippe serait un grand sportif. Leur père serait tout aussi sage et gentil que moi. Il serait pompier et je serais écrivaine. Voilà, la vie que j'aimerais partager avec ma famille!

Catherine Picard 11 ans

Catherine Picard, 11 ans, Otterburn Park, QC
École (Hertel) Au-fil-de-l'eau

Si j'étais une maman, je travaillerais fort pour mes enfants. Je les sur-veillerais comme la prunelle de mes yeux parce que mes enfants ce serait ce qu'il y aurait de plus précieux. J'apprendrais à mes enfants à être polis et respectueux tout en suivant les règles de la maison. Je les prénommerais Caroline et Jean-Philippe. Caroline serait une petite fille travaillante et Jean-Philippe serait un grand sportif. Leur père serait tout aussi sage et gentil que moi. Il serait pompier et je serais écrivaine. Voilà la vie que j'aimerais partager avec ma famille!

If I were the wind I would whisper among the leafy branches of the trees on breezy summer days, but on stormy days, when the trees quiver, I would howl amidst their frantically waving arms. As I drifted along in the sunny spring, I would ruffle the feathers of a bird in flight and touch the cool blue ocean with my gentle fingers. In autumn I could dance through my colorful home. In winter I would be cold -- swirling through the snow, inviting snowflakes to play with me. Oh, what an interesting life the playful wind must have.

Madison Pilling, age 11

Madison Pilling, Age 11, Dartmouth, NS
Caldwell Road School

If I were the wind, I would whisper among the leafy branches of the trees on breezy summer days, but on stormy days when the trees quiver, I would howl amidst their frantically waving arms. As I drifted along in the sunny spring, I would ruffle the feathers of a bird in flight, and touch the cool blue ocean with my gentle fingers. In autumn, I could dance through my colourful home. In winter, I would be cold -- swirling through the snow, inviting snowflakes to play with me. Oh, what an interesting life the playful wind must have.

si j'étais une licorne, je volerais dans le ciel à la recherche de l'éternelle jeunesse. Je laisserai la tristesse loin derrière moi pour voler vers la liberté. Je jourais avec Dame Éternité afin d'avoir l'éternelle jeunesse. J'irais galopper sur un arc-en-ciel pour aller parler avec la lune et le soleil, pour qu'ils me disent le secret de l'éternelle jeunesse. J'irais dans l'espace pour aller glisser sur la Voie lactée et pour enfin aller demander à une étoile ce que c'est le secret de l'éternelle jeunesse. Elle me dirait donc que oui, nous pouvons garder l'éternelle jeunesse, mais dans notre coeur!

Valérie plante 11 ans ½

Valérie Plante, 11 ans, St-Henri, QC
École Belleau

Si j'étais une licorne, je volerais dans le ciel à la recherche de l'éternelle jeunesse. Je laisserais la tristesse loin derrière moi pour voler vers la liberté. Je jouerais avec Dame Éternité afin d'avoir l'éternelle jeunesse. Je vais galoper sur un arc-en-ciel pour aller parler avec la lune et le soleil, pour qu'ils me disent le secret de l'éternelle jeunesse. J'irais dans l'espace pour aller glisser sur la voie lactée et pour enfin aller demander à une étoile ce que c'est le secret de l'éternelle jeunesse. Elle me dirait donc que oui, nous pouvons garder l'éternelle jeunesse, mais dans notre cœur!

Si j'étais le soleil, je brillerais dans le ciel de toutes mes forces pour réchauffer et illuminer le coeur de chaque enfant dans le monde entier. J'utiliserais tout mes rayons pour guider chaque enfant dans un futur prometteur. Je donnerais toute mon énergie pour que chaque personne dorme bien sans avoir froid la nuit. Je partagerais mon éclat à chaque enfant malade pour leur redonner de la couleur, un sourire éclatant et la santé jusqu'à la fin des temps. Après, avoir accomplit tout cela, j'irais me reposer, fier de ma journée.

Vickie Plourde ,12

Vickie Plourde, 12 ans, St-Jacques, NB
École St-Jacques

Si j'étais le soleil, je brillerais dans le ciel de toutes mes forces pour réchauffer et illuminer le cœur de chaque enfant dans le monde entier. J'utiliserais tous mes rayons pour guider chaque enfant dans un futur prometteur. Je donnerais toute mon énergie pour que chaque personne dorme bien sans avoir froid la nuit. Je partagerais mon éclat avec chaque enfant malade pour leur redonner de la couleur, un sourire éclatant et la santé jusqu'à la fin des temps. Après avoir accompli tout cela, j'irais me reposer, fier de ma journée.

If I were... magic, there would be no deaths,
so your life would be full of many breaths.
I'd gather all the poor, and they'd eat apple's to
the core.

If I were magic, no one would fight, it would be as
if we were all close tight. Badness would vanish and
goodness will appear, then no one will have one bit of
fear

If I were magic, there would be no wars, children
would enjoy playing outdoors.

Cancer, disease and sickness would be gone, if only I
could flick my magic wand.

If only I were... magic.

☺ Ashley Poffenroth Age 10

Ashley Poffenroth, Age 10, Calgary, AB
St. Augustine School

If I were magic, there would be no deaths, so your life would be full
of many breaths. I'd gather all poor, and they'd eat the apples to the
core. If I were magic, no one would fight, it would be as if we were
all close tight. Badness would vanish and goodness will appear, then
no one would have one bit of fear. If I were magic, there would be no
wars, children would enjoy playing outdoors. Cancer, disease and
sickness would be gone. If only I could flick my magic wand. If only
I were... magic.

Janie Poirier, 11 ans, Chambly, QC
École Ste-Marie

Si j'étais un brin d'herbe, je discuterais avec les pissenlits. Je ne serais pas heureux si on me piétinerait sans arrêt. Sinon, je ne serais pas en bonne santé et je serais jaune comme un citron. À chaque jour, je regarderais le ciel et je m'imaginerais des dessins dans les nuages tout en admirant le magnifique paysage qui s'étend devant moi. Il y a une chose que je n'aimerais pas que quelqu'un traite la pelouse car sinon les mauvaises herbes, qui sont mes amies meurent. J'aime beaucoup la nuit car personne me marche dessus et je peux regarder les étoiles.

If I were perfect, what a clever, beautiful child I would be! And yet, there would be two different extremes that would be the outcome of the reaction of the children surrounding me: either they would be awed by my perfection in manner, or they would be drawn away from me because of my strange difference from them. Why children are likely to tease others different from them remains a mysterious and poignant question in my heart. Perfection does not always result in what we'd perceive it would. Think of that the next time you put yourself down.

Tara Pollak, Age eleven

Tara Pollak, Age 11, Toronto, ON
Kane Middle School

If I were perfect, what a clever, beautiful child I would be! And yet, there would be two different extremes that would be the outcome of the reaction of the children surrounding me: either they would be awed by my perfection in manner, or they would be drawn away from me because of my strange difference from me. Why children are likely to tease others different from them remains a mysterious and poignant question in my heart. Perfection does not always result in what we'd perceive it would. Think of that the next time you put yourself down.

If I were perfect, what would I do?
Would I take a taxi to Kalamazu?
No! Taxis aren't perfect. How about a slay?
A slay? No way! That would take all day!
And anyways, why Kalamazu?
Why not Texas, or St. John's, or Timbuktu?
Timbuktu isn't perfect! What was I thinking?
Maybe I should sit down and just start lipsinking.
Lipsinking? Thats pointless and silly too!
Maybe I should start by talking to you.
That is, if you want to talk to me.
Or would you perfer to sit and drink tea?
Whatever I do is good because,

I AM PERFECT!

Serena Posner, 9

Serena Posner, Age 9, Toronto, ON
Associated Hebrew Day School

If I were perfect, what would I do? Would I take a taxi to Kalamazu?
No! Taxis aren't perfect. How about a sleigh? A sleigh, no way, that
would take all day! And, anyway, why Kalamazu? Why not Texas or
St. John's or Timbuktu? Timbuktu isn't perfect! What was I thinking?
Maybe I should sit down and just start lipsyncing. Lipsyncing? That's
pointless and silly too. Maybe I should start by talking to you. That is
if you want to talk to me. Or would you prefer to sit and drink tea?
Whatever I do is good because I AM PERFECT!

If I were able to get him back I would. But I'm stuck in here while "Mr. Angel"'s outside. He lied about bombarding me with goo and I got into trouble! Wait! I can get him back! I've got a plan... Ha! Operation slimeball is underway! When my brother opens his door, three buckets of slime will dump on his head! Sshh! Here he comes. He's opening the door, hey!!! Nothing happened! Good! He's gone! Now, let me see... SPLAT! Later... Well, I'm covered in slime and stuck in my room again, for making the trap. But... tomorrow's another day.

Terren Proctor, age 11

Terren Proctor, Age 11, Chateauguay, QC
Children's World Academy

If I were able to get him back, I would. But I'm stuck in here, while Mr. Angel's outside. He lied about bombarding me with goo, and I got into trouble! Wait! I CAN get him back! I've got a plan ... Ha! Operation Slimeball is underway! When my brother opens his door, THREE buckets of slime will dump on his head! Sshh! Here he comes. He's opening the door, hey!!! Nothing happened! Good! He's gone! Now, let me see ... SPLAT! Later... Well, I'm covered in slime and stuck in my room again, for making the trap. But... tomorrow's another day.

If I were the wind, I would swirl, rustle, whisper, whip, sing, zing, fly, bend, turn, sway, unexpectedly flapping the sheets of my friend, the sailboat.

Without me you are lulled.

I am what makes your ropes dance.

I am what makes the waves roll.

You are tied to the dock like a puppy on a leash. Excited. Overjoyed. I am calling your name so come on, let's play!

Hanna Quathamer 9

Hanna Quathamer, Age 9, Arnprior, ON
St Joseph's Elementary School

If I were the wind I would swirl, rustle, whisper, whip, sing, zing, fly, bend, turn, sway, unexpectedly flapping the sheets of my friend, the sailboat. Without me you are lulled. I am what makes your ropes dance. I am what makes the waves roll. You are tied to the dock like a puppy on a leash. Excited. Overjoyed. I am calling your name so come on, let's play!

If I were a river I would flow over hills
I'd flow over mountains and flow at my
will. In winter, Ice would form over me
but in the spring time it would break
free. I'd go over Niagra Falls and crash
into man made walls. Little streams
would come with me just to see where
I have been. When the skies above
cry it would make my tides go high.
Birds and docks would ride, just
until the highest tide. I'd flow in rain
I'd flow in sun, evrey time I flow I
have fun.

Morag Ramsey , 11

Morag Ramsey, Age 11, Campbell River, BC
École des deux mondes

If I were a river I would flow over hills I'd flow over mountains and
flow at my will. In winter, ice would form over me but in the springtime it would break free. I'd go over Niagara Falls and crash into
man-made walls. Little streams would come with me just to see were
I have been. When the skies above cry it would make my tides go
high. Birds and ducks would ride, just until the highest tide. I'd flow
in rain I'd flow in sun, every time I flow I have fun.

Si j'étais Cupidon, l'ange des amoureux, je ferais deux choses.
Premièrement, je ferais apparaître une
échelle qui me mènerait au ciel.
Je m'asseoirais sur un nuage
éloigné pour voir le monde entier.
Là-haut, je couvrirais mes yeux
d'un ruban bleu. Avec ce ruban
magique, je lancerais des flèches
tout autour. Peut-être qu'ainsi
la Terre serait inondée de paix
et de fraternité, pour que
l'humanité s'offre un futur
ensoleillé!

La deuxième chose que je ferais,
si j'étais Cupidon, j'enfilerais vite
un pantalon!
          Mélanie Rioux, 12 ans

Mélanie Rioux, 12 ans, Lac-Beauport, QC
École Saint-Jean-Eudes

Si j'étais Cupidon, l'ange des amoureux, je ferais deux choses.
Premièrement, je ferais apparaître une échelle qui me mènerait au ciel.
Je m'asseoirais sur un nuage éloigné pour voir le monde entier. Là-
haut, je couvrirais mes yeux d'un ruban bleu. Avec ce ruban magique,
je lancerais des flèches tout autour. Peut-être qu'ainsi, la Terre serait
inondée de paix et de fraternité pour que l'humanité s'offre un futur
ensoleillé! La deuxième chose que je ferais, si j'étais Cupidon:
j'enfilerais vite un pantalon!

If I were...a butterfly, I would soar through the sky so high. I would fly all day, nothing would get in my way. One day in the future, I will be a butterfly, and this is how my life would go. Last night I slept in a tree, It was pretty big. I met my best friend, Monarch, she's nice. We went soaring high through the sky today. Tonight I'm sleeping in a pile of sticks. Fall quickly passed. Monarch didn't make it, she got eaten by a snake. I will die soon, and that's the life of butterflies.

Shannon Rizzato, age 11

Shannon Rizzato, Age 11, Lingan, NS
Greenfield Elementary School

If I were a butterfly, I would soar through the sky so high. I would fly all day, nothing would get in my way. One day in the future, I will be a butterfly and this is how my life would go. Last night I slept in a tree, it was pretty big. I met my best friend, Monarch, she's nice. We went soaring high through the sky today. Tonight I'm sleeping in a pile of sticks. Fall quickly passed. Monarch didn't make it, she got eaten by a snake. I will die soon, and that's the life of butterflies.

Si j'étais un Chaton, je
Serait mignon. Et si j'étais
un chaton, Voici une aventure
que je ferais. Un jour
il y avait un chat
qui a eu ses premiers
petits:, un noir, un blanc
et un calico. Un jour
moi le noir est allé
me promener dans la forêt.
J'ai chassé les papillons et
j'ai grimper les arbres. Je
me suis bien amusé. Un
loup m'a vu! Il n'était
pas gentil. Il m'a chassé
coer j'étais coincé! Mais ma
mère l'a grafigné. J'étais en
trouble d'être allé dans la forêt.
           Abigale Robertson - Age: 11 ans

Abigale Robertson, 11 ans, Legal, AB
École Citadelle

Si j'étais un chaton, je serais mignon. Et si j'étais un chaton, voici une
aventure que je fairais. Un jour il y avait un chat qui a eu ses premiers
petits; un noir, un blanc et un calico. Un jour moi le noir est allé me
promener dans la forêt. J'ai chassé les papillons et j'ai grimpé les
arbres. Je me suis bien amusé. Un loup m'a vu! Il n'était pas gentil.
Il m'a chassé car j'étais coincé. Mais ma mère l'a grafigné. J'étais
en trouble d'être allé dans la forêt.

If I were a tree, I'd start as a seed. My time would come, and I'd shoot out as a sprout. Over the years, I'd continue to grow. My roots would dig deeper into the healthy soil. My branches would bud and leaves would emerge. In the springtime, my leaves would be fresh and green. When summer arrives, I'd become more beautiful, with tiny, white flowers covering my great boughs, and fruit growing within. In autumn, I'd be spectacular. With leaves of red, orange, and brown. In the winter, I'd be leafless, but not lifeless. I'd await spring's renewal.

Sean Robinon 12

Sean Robinon, Age 12, Amherstburg, ON
Malden Central Public School

If I were a tree, I'd start as a seed. My time would come, and I'd shoot out as a sprout. Over the years, I'd continue to grow. My roots would dig deeper into the healthy soil. My branches would bud and leaves would emerge. In the springtime, my leaves would be fresh and green. When summer arrives, I'd become more beautiful with tiny, white flowers covering my great boughs, and fruit growing within. In autumn, I'd be spectacular, with leaves of red, orange, and brown. In the winter I'd be leafless, but not lifeless. I'd await spring's renewal.

If I were a dragon I'd have a breath of fire. I'd also have big wings that I could fly with. I would live in a magical land where other magical creatures lived, like unicorns and seamonsters. I would live in a cave in a mountain. I would gaurd a pile of gold and other treasures. I'd have whatever I wanted and would live a happy life. My life would be a lot different if I were a dragon but I'm happy I'm human.

Andrew Rockwell 11

Andrew Rockwell, Age 11, Enfield, NS
Riverside Education Center

If I were a dragon I'd have a breath of fire. I'd also have big wings that I could fly with. I would live in a magical land where other magical creatures lived, like unicorns and seamonsters. I would live in a cave in a mountain. I would guard a pile of gold and other treasures. I'd have whatever I wanted and would live a happy life. My life would be a lot different if I was a dragon. But I'm happy I'm human.

If I were a red Lego brick, I would face many fun times and perilous adventures. I'd start out life shiny and new in a Lego Rebel Blockade Runner set....... Daniel brought me home from the store and built the Runner. Daniel's friends came to play and they took the Runner apart and built spaceships using me. Then, Daniel's Mom said,"Time to clean up for lunch." I was tossed aside and separated from the other Lego pieces. The next thing I remember is being hauled from the vacuum less shiny and red. Now, it was time for another adventure!

Daniel J.W. Rose, 9

Daniel J.W. Rose, Age 9, Kingston, ON
J.E. Horton Public School

If I were a red Lego brick, I would face many fun times and perilous adventures. I'd start out life shiny and new in a Lego 'Rebel Blockade Runner' set ... Daniel brought me home from the store and built the runner. Daniel's friends came to play and they took the runner apart and built spaceships using me. Then, Daniel's mom said "Time to clean up for lunch." I was tossed aside and separated from the other Lego pieces. The next thing I remember is being hauled from the vacuum, less shiny and red. Now, it was time for another adventure!

If I were a grand piano I would travel into the music that the person was playing. I would want to hear jazz through my strings and feel the heat of the lights shining down on me. Many musicians would come on the stage to play me - some classical, choral, romance, and blues. I will proudly raise my lid so you can hear my rich, full sound echoing row by row going down the isles. I would like to end my musical journey by settling into the home of a young girl who loves to play me.

Janelle Santi, 8

Janelle Santi, Age 8, Kitchener, ON
St. Paul School

If I were a grand piano, I would travel into the music that the person was playing. I would want to hear jazz through my strings and feel the heat of the lights shining down on me. Many musicians would come on the stage to play me -- some classical, choral, romance, and blues. I will proudly raise my lid so you can hear my rich, full sound echoing row by row, going down the aisles. I would like to end my musical journey by settling into the home of a young girl who loves to play me.

185

If I were an eagle soaring high and free, if I were an eagle soaring superbly, if I were an eagle soaring high and low, if I were an eagle soaring very slow; if I were a monkey swinging from tree to tree, if I were a monkey swinging one two three, if I were a monkey swinging round the bend, if I were a monkey swinging with no end. If I were either of those things it might be kind of fun, but as you know I'm neither of those things so I might as well just be me.

by Anne Savidge, age 9

Anne Savidge, Age 9, Fredericton, NB
Our Lady of Grace School

If I were an eagle soaring high and free, if I were an eagle soaring superbly, if I were an eagle soaring high and low, if I were an eagle soaring very slow; if I were a monkey swinging from tree to tree, if I were a monkey swinging one, two, three; if I were a monkey swinging 'round the bend, if I were a monkey swinging with no end. If I were either of those things, it might be kind of fun, but as you know, I'm neither of those things, so I might as well just be me.

If I were a star, I would shine down on the people. It would be fun to light up the sky! At night when nobody would look, I'd shoot across the sky with little sparkles following me! Then I would put on my night-cap and go to sleep. When the sun comes up and the rooster goes "Cock-a-doodle-doo," I'd shoot to the other side of the world. Then I'd go back to sleep. Later I'd make breakfast with the big dipper. I'd have to keep track of time so I could buy a parka for the Arctic.

Maria Schigol, 8

Maria Schigol, Age 8, Canora, SK
Canora Junior Elementary School

If I were a star, I would shine down on the people. It would be fun to light up the sky! At night, when nobody would look, I'd shoot across the sky with little sparkles following me! Then I would put on my nightcap and go to sleep. When the sun comes up, and the rooster goes "Cock-a-doodle-doo," I'd shoot to the other side of the world. Then I'd go back to sleep. Later, I'd make breakfast with the Big Dipper. I'd have to keep track of the time so I could buy a parka for the Arctic.

If I were a space scientist I would be the first person to go to every planet in the universe in a short while. Also I would bring small chunks of every comet from every planet. Then I will find any mineral from the chunks of the comets and use it to make a chemical that can decompose any kind of plastic. Using this I will help the planet earth from pollution. So that the planet earth would be a better place to live. Also scientists can make any more plastics to improve our technology without pollution.

Shreeram Senthivasan 8years

Shreeram Senthivasan, Age 8, Scarborough, ON
Birchcliff Public School

If I were a space scientist, I would be the first person to go to every planet in the universe in a short while. Also, I would bring small chunks of every comet from every planet. Then I will find any mineral from the chunks of the comets and use it to make a chemical that can decompose any kind of plastic. Using this, I will help the planet Earth from pollution. So that the planet Earth would be a better place to live. Also, scientists can make any more plastics to improve our technology without pollution.

If I were... God I would promote world peace by creating more tolerance of each other. There would be no borders and all people treated equally. I would solve starvation by putting a vegetable garden in some yards and others would receive grains and animals. This would encourage sharing the gifts of food together. If I were God I would deal with racism by making everyone the same colour so there would be no objection to the colour of a persons skin only acceptance of anothers individual thoughts and feelings. This would be a world to contemplate and strive for...

Cameron Simmons, 12

Cameron Simmons, Age 12, Kamloops, BC
McGowan Park Elementary School

If I were God I would promote world peace by creating more tolerance of each other. There would be no borders and all people treated equally. I would solve starvation by putting a vegetable garden in some yards and others would receive grains and animals. This would encourage sharing the gifts of food together. If I were God I would deal with racism by making everyone the same colour so there would be no objection to the colour of a person's skin, only acceptance of another's individuals thoughts and feelings. This would be a world to contemplate and strive for...

If I were my mother,
I would have to work too hard,
If I were my father,
I'd run a thousand yards.
If I were a police girl,
I would have to fight crime,
and If I were a convict,
I would have to do some time.
If I were a clown,
I'd have to be real happy,
And If I were a crocodile,
I would be real snappy.
If I were a teacher,
I would teach people like me,
and If I were a waitress,
I would serve people tea.
No, I'd much rather be me!
Holly Sinclair Age 9

Holly Sinclair, Age 9, Ottawa, ON
Fielding Drive Public School

If I were my mother, I would have to work too hard. If I were my father, I'd run a thousand yards. If I were a police girl, I would have to fight crime, and if I were a convict, I'd have to do some time. If I were a clown, I'd have to be real happy, and if I were a crocodile, I would be really snappy. If I were a teacher, I would teach people like me, and if I were a waitress, I would serve people tea. No, I'd much rather be me!!!!

If I were in a place where people wore cats instead of hats, and the horses ran free past purple paper trees. A place where people had to pay one golden ticket to play a game of cricket, and pigs with funny little wigs ate figs on bunny shaped clouds.
A place where apes swing on grapes, with thier polka dot pet snakes in cages, where swans swim in ponds of jellybeans.
A place where dreams could come true, and the sky would be orange, instead of light blue.
Well, I'd say that place is magnificent! Wouldn't you agree too?

Michelle Smith age 11

Michelle Smith, Age 11, Brampton, ON
Homestead Public School

If I were in a place where people wore cats instead of hats, and the horses ran free past purple paper trees. A place where people had to pay one golden ticket to play a game of cricket, and pigs with funny little wigs ate figs on bunny-shaped clouds. A place where apes swing on grapes, their polka-dot pet snakes in cages, where swans swim in ponds of jelly beans. A place where dreams could come true, and the skies are orange instead of light blue. Well, I'd say that place is magnificent, wouldn't you agree too?

"If I were you, Human," smiled the dragon, "I'd run for my life." The stable boy was not well protected. He wore a barrel for armour and carried a hand made spear. The dragon took a deep breath and blew fire from its mouth! Flames scorched the wooden armour. At that moment, the boy took up the spear, hurtling it toward the dragon. It flew right into its heart. The dragon staggered back. There was a blinding light. When it was gone, all that lay there was the spear. The dragon was defeated. "Maybe you should've run," answered the boy.

Dana Kurt Sorensen, age 12

Dana Kurt Sorensen, Age 12, Ottawa, ON
Emily Carr Middle School

"If I were you, Human," smiled the dragon, "I'd run for my life."
The stable boy was not well protected. He wore a barrel for armour and carried a hand-made spear. The Dragon took a deep breath and blew fire from it's mouth! Flames scorched the wooden armour. At that moment, the boy took up the spear, hurtling it toward the dragon. It flew right into its heart. The dragon staggered back. There was a blinding light. When it was gone, all that lay there was the spear. The dragon was defeated. "Maybe you should've run," answered the boy.

Si j'étais un humain, y leur dirais ma façon de penser! Mais je ne suis qu'une rose, je ne peux hurler ma douleur lorsequ'ils m'arrachent de mon sol, je ne puis leur dirais la torture du souffle coupé quand une ombre s'affale sur moi. ILS m'utilisent comme signe d'amour. ILS m'offrent en présent comme l'on offre une cage à un oiseau et qu'on est tout fier de sa trouvaille. EGOÏSTES! Le rouge de mes pétales ne représente pas l'amour, ni la passion. Le rouge d'une rose reflète le sang qui ruiselle sur une joue. C'est notre seule façon de parler.

Takwa Souissi, 13 ans

Takwa Souissi, 13 ans, St-Laurent, QC
École St-Laurent, Pavillon Émile Legault

Si j'étais un humain, je leur dirais ma façon de penser! Mais je ne suis qu'une rose, je ne peux hurler ma douleur lorsqu'ils m'arrachent de mon sol, je ne puis leur décrire la torture du souffle coupé quand une ombre s'affale sur moi. Ils m'utilisent comme signe d'amour. Ils m'offrent en présent comme l'on offre une cage à un oiseau et qu'on est tout fier de sa trouvaille. Égoïstes! Le rouge de mes pétales ne représente pas l'amour, ni la passion. Le rouge d'une rose reflète le sang qui ruisselle sur une joue. C'est notre seule façon de parler.

If I were a blade of grass, I would get stepped on every single day. I would freeze in the winter and grow in the summer. Children would play on me, sit on me, and dogs would tear me out by my roots. I would take in carbon dioxide and make it into fresh air. Also, life would be better if no one had a lawn mower. I would have thousands of friends. My favorite kinds of days would be it rains, then slows down to a few drops, and finally the sun comes out.

Alisa Stamp, 12

Alisa Stamp, Age 12, Enoch, AB
Kitaskinaw School

If I were a blade of grass I would get stepped on every single day.
I would freeze in the winter and grow in the summer. Children would
play on me, sit on me, and dogs would tear me out by my roots.
I would take in carbon dioxide and make it into fresh air. Also, life
would be better if no one had a lawnmower. I would have thousands
of friends. My favourite kinds of days would be when it rains, then
slows down to a few drops, and finally the sun comes out.

If I were President, listen to this,
Read it over carefully so there's
nothing you miss.
Our world would be as perfect as
can be,
We would all fit together like honey
and a bee.
All the countries are everyones land,
We would all get together hand in
hand.
We would never be bored and there
would be no tax.
Everyone can sit back and relax.
There would be no wars and no one
would be mean,
"Pop" I just woke up from my
dream.

Samantha Stanga

Samantha Stanga, Age 12, Prince Albert, SK
Red Wing School

If I were President, listen to this, read it over carefully so there's nothing you miss, our world would be as perfect as can be, like honey and a bee. All the countries are everyones land, we all get together hand in hand. We would never be bored and there would be no tax, everyone can sit back and relax. There would be no wars and no one would be mean, "Pop" I just woke up from my dream.

If I were to pass you on the street,
I'd wish for you a home and lots to eat.
A warm bed at night wouldn't that
be nice, instead of a doorway all
frozen with ice. Family to hug you upon
your return. A warm cozy fire to sit
and watch burn. Perhaps a pet to
sleep by your knee, as the lights danced
and twinkled upon the trees. These
things I wish in passing my friend, may
your journey of lonliness soon come
to an end.

Amanda Stevens. Age: 12

Amanda Stevens, Age 12, Toronto, ON
West Hill Public School

If I were to pass you on the street, I'd wish for you a home and lots to
eat. A warm bed at night wouldn't that be nice, instead of a doorway all
frozen with ice. Family to hug you upon your return. A warm cozy fire
to sit and watch burn. Perhaps a pet to sleep by your knee, as the lights
danced and twinkled upon the trees. These things I wish in passing my
friend, may your journey of loneliness soon come to an end.

If I were a paintbrush, I would make someone's life more colourful, avoiding the dullness that person may see or assume about themselves. I would colour in their personality and dreams, making them look more appealing, instead of seeing themselves as a failure. I would continue to brighten people's lives when a shadow is casting upon them. The day will come when all my bristles will have been torn or fallen off. The colour that I had put into all those people's lives, will continue to shine brighter, making them feel more secure, confident and happy about themselves.

Meaghan Sullivan, 13

Meaghan Sullivan, Age 13, Mount Albert, ON
Our Lady of Good Counsel School

If I were a paintbrush, I would make someone's life more colourful, avoiding the dullness that people may see or assume about themselves. I would colour in their personality and dreams, making them look more appealing, instead of seeing themselves as becoming a failure. I would continue to brighten people's lives when a shadow has been cast upon them. The day will come when all my bristles will be torn or fallen off. The colour that I had put into all those people's lives will continue to shine brighter, making them feel more secure, confident and happy about themselves.

If I were... a caterpillar what would life be like? Crawling across the hot cement I'd sweat and burn my toes off. It's dangerous and scary. These big black birds come and try to eat me but I'm safe for I am camouflaged in the deep green bushes. Time has come! I must hurry and think fast. I spin my silk cocoon and wait for my rebirth. Days pass which turn into weeks. Finally I'm alive!! How beautiful I look! My wings sparkling in the sun, I glide care free through the crisp summer air. I'm happy! I'm set free!

Michelle Tagliafierro, 12

Michelle Tagliafierro, Age 12, Sudbury, ON
St. David School

If I were a caterpillar what would life be like? Crawling across the hot cement I'd sweat and burn my toes off. It's dangerous and scary. These big black birds come and try to eat me but I'm safe for I am camouflaged in the deep green bushes. Time has come! I must hurry and think fast. I spin my silk cocoon and wait for my rebirth. Days pass which turn into weeks. Finally I'm alive!! How beautiful I look! My wings sparkling in the sun, I glide care free through the crisp summer air. I'm happy! I'm set free!

Si j'étais une boucle d'oreille je pourrais écouter tout ce que le monde dit: leurs petits secrets, leurs petites bêtises et d'autres petits mots d'amours. Ah! c'est ados! ils disent tout plein de bêtises, comme Frédérick et ses ami(e)s. Ils en dise pres que tout le temps. Des fois, Frédérick m'échange contre une épingle à couche. Ça me donne le temps de me reposer. Mais deux ou trois jours après, je retourne sur son oreille. Des fois, je me demande si j'étais un ados comment serait ma vie. Je me le demande à chaque jour de la semaine Bey Bey à la prochaine!

Frédérick Taillefer st-onge 12 ans

Frédérick Taillefer St-Onge, 12 ans, Laval, QC
École Vanguard

Si j'étais une boucle d'oreille, je pourrais écouter tout ce que le monde dit: leurs petits secrets, leurs petites bêtises et d'autres petits mots d'amour. Ah! ces ados! Ils disent tout plein de bêtises, comme Frédérick et ses ami(e)s. Ils en disent presque tout le temps. Des fois, Frédérick m'échange contre une épingle à couche. Ça me donne le temps de me reposer. Mais deux ou trois jours après, je retourne sur son oreille. Des fois, je me demande si j'étais un ado comment serait ma vie. Je me le demande à chaque jour de la semaine. Bye Bye, à la prochaine!

> "If I were stranded on an island...." I never thought that would happen, but when my helicopter crashed, I knew it wasn't a dream. There was no way of getting back, so I learned to cope. There was plenty of underbrush for fires, and some sturdy logs and thick branches around a tree made a dwelling. For food I milked goats and made cheese. There were lots of edible plants, and sometimes I had bear when I had to spear down an attacking one I sure learned to live with nature. Being stranded isn't that bad after all!
>
> Sarah Taylor, age 9

Sarah Taylor, Age 9, Kelowna, BC
Kelowna Christian School

"If I were stranded on an island…" I never thought that would happen, but when my helicopter crashed, I knew it wasn't a dream. There was no way of getting back, so I learned to cope. There was plenty of underbrush for fires, and some sturdy logs and thick branches around a tree made a dwelling. For food I milked goats and made cheese. There were lots of edible plants, and sometimes I had bear when I had to spear down an attacking one. I sure learned to live with nature. Being stranded isn't that bad after all!

If I were a dot, I could
be a period in a line of my
favourite song. I could be a
freckle on my friend's face. If I
were a dot on a ladybug's wing,
I could fly. If I were a dot, I could
be a spot on a banana and be
rotten for a while. If I were a
dot, I could be a note of
music and people would play me.
I could be a spot on a dalmation
dog, or a dot on my soccer ball,
or the dot in an eagle's eye, and
I'd fly.

Cole Thompson age 9

Cole Thompson, Age 9, Vernon, BC
Beairsto School

If I were a dot, I could be a period in a line of my favourite song.
I could be a freckle on my friend's face. If I were a dot on a lady
bug's wing, I could fly. If I were a dot, I could be a spot on a banana,
and be rotten for a while. If I were a dot, I could be a note of music,
and people would play me. I could be a spot on a Dalmation dog,
or a dot on my soccer ball, or the dot in an eagle's eye, and I'd fly.

If I were a Fireman
I would drive a Firetruck.
I would use a hose to put
out the Fire. when the alarm
rings I would go into the
Firetruck drive Fast and I
would go into the house and
Put out the Fire. There was
another call and it was a
Forest fire, I helped the
other firemen Put it out. When
I was done I would go back
to the Fire Station, have a
Snack then go to bed. Then I
would do it all over again
the next day.

JACK Tolton 5

Jack Tolton, Age 5, Walkerton, ON
Brant Central Public School

If I were a fireman, I would drive a fire truck. I would use a hose to
put out the fire. When the alarm rings, I would go into the fire truck,
drive fast, and I would go into the house and put out the fire. There
was another call and it was a forest fire. I helped the other firemen put
it out. When I was done, I would go back to the fire station, have a
snack, then go to bed. Then I would do it all over again the next day.

If I were the moon I'd see the wonderful things of our fascinating world: things way beyond my imagination. I'd see the men that work day and night having the confidence that they might make something that will change the world. Their dream would be that their name would be written in history. They would be like the Wright brothers or Thomas Edison. Maybe they might make a teleporter that can make packages go around the world faster than the speed of light. I have to shine away now to catch a falling star and put it in my pocket!

Paul Samuel Jones 10

Paul Samuel Torres, Age 10, Pickering, ON
FaithWay Baptist School

If I were the moon, I'd see the wonderful things of our fascinating world, things way beyond my imagination. I'd see the men that work day and night having the confidence that they might make something that will change the world. Their dream would be that their name would be written in history. They would be like the Wright Brothers or Thomas Edison. Maybe they might make a teleporter that can make packages go around the world faster than the speed of light! I have to shine away now to catch a falling star and put it in my pocket.

"If I were a dog, I could forget about homework"
(Dog→) "If I were a person, I could forget about
fleas." (Person→) "If I were a dog, I wouldn't
worry about eating broccoli." (Dog→) "If I
were human I could have more than mutt
chow!" (Person→) "A dog doesn't have to
do chores!" (Dog→) "Being human I could
walk any time." (Person→) "I could scream
really loud and jump up and down." (Dog→)
"Unlimited snacks and a warm cozy bed...."
(Both)
     "I wish I could be more like him!"

Megan Tromposch, 11

Megan Tromposch, Age 11, Bragg Creek, AB
Banded Peak School

"If I were a dog, I could forget about homework. (Dog): "If I were a person, I could forget about fleas." (Person): " If I were a dog, I wouldn't worry about eating broccoli." (Dog): "If I were a human, I could have more than mutt chow." (Person): "A dog doesn't have to do chores!" (Dog): "Being human, I could walk anytime." (Person): "I could scream really loud and jump up and down." (Dog): "Unlimited snacks and a warm cozy bed..." (Both): "I wish I could be more like him!"

Si j'étais un poisson je ferais le tour de l'Atlantique. Je ferais beaucoup de tours de bateaux car je serais un poisson spécial. Je me ferais une belle maison dans un coquillage. J'aurais beaucoup d'amis. Je voyagerais dans tous les pays du monde. Je serais un poisson clown. J'aurais un beau lit dans une huître. Je jouerais au ballon avec une perle avec mon ami le poisson-lune. Mon plat préféré serait les algues rouges. Mais il faudrait que je fasse attention aux requins pour ne pas qu'ils me mangent. Ah! si j'étais un poisson ce serait merveilleux!

Sarah-Jeanne turgeon   7 ans

Sarah-Jeanne Turgeon, 7 ans, Beaconsfield, QC
École St-Rémi

Si j'étais un poisson, je ferais le tour de l'Atlantique. Je ferais beaucoup de tours de bateau car je serais un poisson spécial. Je me ferais une belle maison dans un coquillage. J'aurais beaucoup d'amis. Je voyagerais dans tous les pays du monde. Je serais un poisson clown. J'aurais un beau lit dans une huître. Je jouerais du ballon avec une perle avec mon ami le poisson-lune. Mon plat préféré serait les algues rouges. Mais il faudrait que je fasse attention aux requins pour ne pas qu'ils me mangent. Ah! si j'étais un poisson, ce serait merveilleux!

Si j'étais... Si j'étais... mais qu'est-ce que je pourrais être? Électricien? Non, je risquerais de m'emmêler dans mes fils. Professeur? Non, je serais trop gêné devant la classe. Marin? Non, moi les vagues ça me donne le mal de mer. Fermier? Non, j'aurais le rhume des foins. Éboueur? Beurk! Gardien de zoo? Et me faire manger par le lion! Non! Je crois que je ferais mieux de ne pas y penser tout de suite. Je suis encore trop jeune pour décider. D'ailleurs, je dois me préparer pour l'école. À moins que... chercheur? Voilà je pourrais chercher un métier.

Hubert Vallée, 8 ans

Hubert Vallée, 8 ans, Sainte-Foy, QC
École St-Louis-de-France II

Si j'étais... Si j'étais... mais qu'est-ce que je pourrais être? Électricien?
Non, je risquerais de m'emmêler dans mes fils. Professeur? Non, je
serais trop gêné devant la classe. Marin? Non, moi les vagues ça me
donne le mal de mer. Fermier? Non, j'aurais le rhume des foins.
Éboueur? Beurk! Gardien de zoo? Et me faire manger par le lion! Non!
Je crois que je ferais mieux de ne pas y penser tout de suite. Je suis
encore trop jeune pour décider. D'ailleurs, je dois me préparer pour l'é-
cole. À moins que... chercheur? Voilà, je pourrais chercher un métier.

If I were a mad genus that could make things, I would make a machine that goes back in time to dinosaur life. I would meet some dinosaurs and become friends. I would get stuck because my machine got broke and all my tools were back at my house. I woold build a new house with branches from trees. I would make a fisbee out of sticks to play with my dinosaur in the end my would make tools to fix my machine but I would decide to stay with my dinosaurs.
Travis van Engelen age 5

Travis van Engelen, Age 5, Brampton, ON
Russel D. Barber School

If I were a mad genius that could make things, I would make a machine that goes back in time to dinosaur life. I would meet some dinosaurs and become friends. I would get stuck because my machine got broke and all my tools were back at my house. I would build a new house with branches from trees. I would make a frisbee out of sticks to play with my dinosaur. In the end I would make tools to fix my machine, but I would decide to stay with my dinosaurs.

If I were an Indian girl, one hundred years ago, I would help the adults build one of the tepees made of sticks and cloth. Then I would invite all the Indians to a special feast. We would sit around the crackling warm fire and eat buffalo meat with berries, plump and sweet and good. We would dance to the beautiful, exciting music; the banging of the drums, the jingling of bells, the clanging of sticks and the stomping of our feet. We would sing in great harmony and feel as if we were flying high up in the sky.

Louise Veenstra, 7

Louise Veenstra, Age 7, Taber, AB
Dr. Hamman School

If I were an Indian girl, one hundred years ago, I would help the adults build one of the tallest teepees made of sticks and cloth. Then, I would invite all the Indians to a special feast. We would sit around the crackling warm fire and eat buffalo meat with berries, plump and sweet and good. We would dance to the beautiful, exciting music, the banging of drums, the jingling of bells, the clanging of sticks and the stomping of our feet. We would sing in great harmony and feel as if we were flying high up in the sky.

If I were a novel I'd be a wonderful classic. My reader would keep me on a shelf where only the best books are kept. My smooth, hard cover would be worn at the edges. Some of my pages would be falling out, but that wouldn't matter because my reader would know exactly what order they went in. As my reader opened my pages, he'd be lured into a world of suspense and mystery, promising to keep him on the edge of his seat. I'd be passed down through the generations, being remembered by each reader as an unforgettable masterpiece.

Shelby Vilneff, age 13

Shelby Vilneff, Age 13, Marmora, ON
Sacred Heart School

If I were a novel, I'd be a wonderful classic. My reader would keep me on a shelf where only the best books are kept. My smooth, hard cover would be worn at the edges. Some of my pages would be falling out, but that wouldn't matter because my reader would know exactly what order they went in. As my reader opened my pages, he'd be lured into a world of suspense and mystery, promising to keep him on the edge of his seat. I'd be passed down through the generations, being remembered by each reader as an unforgettable masterpiece.

"If I were still young," I thought as I watched four year old Kandas splashing in the rain from my kitchen window. She was singing happily as the warm raindrops slid down her back. When she noticed I was watching she called, "come join me Alice!"

"Oh Kandas," I replied, "at my age?" Sadly Kandas continued splashing, the skip gone from her feet. Remembering my earlier thought I shouted, "Kandas I'm coming!" Kandas's face was beaming as I ran down the walk. I took her hand in mine and we walked towards the rainbow, singing, in the rain.

Angela Waldner – 13

Angela Waldner, Age 13, Sperling, MB
Silverwinds School

"If I were still young," I thought, as I watched four-year-old Kandas splashing in the rain from my kitchen window. She was singing happily as the warm raindrops slid down her back. When she noticed I was watching, she called, "Come join me, Alice!" "Oh Kandas," I replied, "...at my age?" Sadly Kandas continued splashing, the skip gone from her feet. Remembering my earlier thought, I shouted, "Kandas, I'm coming!" Kandas' face was beaming as I ran down the walk. I took her hand in mine and we walked towards the rainbow singing ... in the rain.

If I were a skunk my life would be hectic, running around, scavenging for food and annoying campers. When they're around campfires, I'm looking for hot-dog buns. If I'm lucky I'll find a couple of macaroni noodles on the ground. Also I'd never have to go to school. Just eat, drink, run and spray people all day. I'd have to avoid people though (or try to!) and bigger animals that would try to eat me. The beautiful, lush and luxurious forest would be my home. It's all part of being a skunk. Overall life would be spectacular!!

Rebecca Webb, 12

Rebecca Webb, Age 12, Lorraine, QC
Rosemere High School

If I were a skunk my life would be hectic, running around, scavenging for food and annoying campers. When they're around campfires, I'm looking for hot-dog buns. If I'm lucky I'll find macaroni noodles on the ground. Also, I'd never have to go to school. Just eat, run, spray people and drink all day. I'd have to avoid people though, also, avoid bigger animals and things that could eat me. The beautiful, lush and luxurious forest would be my home. It's all part of being a skunk. Overall, life would be spectacular.

If I were a piece of gum my story would go somewhat like this... after ages of sitting on a shelf in a pack I was bought. I had been bought by a young boy who was going to hollywood for a vacation. He chewed me on the plane (not a pleasant experience) then spat me out on his way to the hotel. I was then stepped on by, get this, Leonardo DiCaprio! with me on his shoe Leonardo went to come fancy restaurant, Cher Cher I think. Together we stoped at the little boys room where he trashed me

Em Whalen, age 11

Em Whalen, Age 11, Pitt Meadows, BC
Pitt Meadows Elementary School

If I were a piece of gum, my story would go somewhat like this...
After ages of sitting on a shelf in a pack, I was bought. I had been
bought by a young boy who was going to Hollywood for a vacation.
He chewed me on the plane (not a pleasant experience), then spat me
out on his way to the hotel. I was then stepped on by, get this,
Leonardo DiCaprio! With me on his shoe, Leonardo went to some
fancy restaurant, 'Cher Cher', I think. Together, we stopped at the
little boys' room, where he trashed me.

If I were a caterpillar, as busy as can be, I would live in my house at the top of the coconut tree. I have a friend Bee you see, she is very nice to me! We play games like Chess and Guess-who. Without her I think I'd go koo-koo! We knit and sew and even dosey-doe.

She has a cousin Moe, that has a show that is a parade of fleas. We laugh so hard we fall to our knees!

If you were a caterpiller as busy as me, I don't know where you would be! Do you know!

Kaila Wilson, age 12

Kaila Wilson, Age 12, La Salle, ON
Oakwood Public School

If I were a caterpillar, as busy as can be, I would live in my house at the top of the coconut tree. I have a friend Bee, you see, she is very nice to me! We play games like chess and guess-who. Without her, I think I'd go koo-koo! We knit and sew, and even dosey-doe. She has a cousin Moe, who has a show, that is a parade of fleas. We laugh so hard, we fall to our knees! If you were a caterpillar as busy as me, I don't know where you would be. Do you know?

"If I were.... A what?" James said quietly. He'd been at this for ages now. Trying to think of what he would be in his story. The contest was interesting. The prizes were more than he could imagine, too! "Now, what could I be.." He thought to himself. A Mayor? No... "Hmm.." he mused over his cereal. Maybe a Duchess? No... It's Duke anyways. "You're sure writing a lot!" said his sister. "You're like one of those book writers?" "An Author?" He asked. "Yeah?" said his sister. An author.. Thats what I'll be! An Author?

Sam Wolfe, 9

Sam Wolfe, Age 9, North Vancouver, BC
Dorothy Lynas Elementary School

If I were... "A what?" James said quietly. He'd been at this for ages now. Trying to think of what he would be in his story. The contest was interesting, the prizes were more than he could imagine too! "Now, what could I be...," he thought to himself, "...a Mayor? No... Hmm...," he mused over his cereal. "...maybe a Duchess! No... it's a DUKE, anyways." "You're sure writing a lot!" said his sister. "You're like one of those book writers!" "An author?" he asked. "Yeah!" said his sister. An author... That's what I'll be! An author!

If I were a flag, I would be raised up a pole each day. There I may sit, watching the world move on. People all around could express joy in me, a one-of-a-kind flag of their nation. I will be proud of my job, my duty, and myself. At which time the rain drops hard, and the wind blows furiously, I will sit there bravely, acknowledging the end of my reign. Torn into shreds, I will watch a replacement being raised. If I were a beautiful, one-of-a-kind flag, I would serve my country well.

Chapmann Wong; Age 11

Chapmann Wong, Age 11, Vancouver, BC
Osler School

If I were a flag, I would be raised up a pole each day. There I may sit, watching the world move on. People all around could express joy in me, a one-of-a-kind flag of their nation. I will be proud of my job, my duty, and myself. At which time, the rain drops hard, and the wind blows furiously. I will sit there bravely, acknowledging the end of my reign. Torn into shreds, I will watch a replacement being raised. If I were a beautiful, one-of-a-kind flag, I would serve my country well.

If I were your shadow, I would go wherever you go. Jump with you and walk with you. I can't guide you, but i'll be with you until you die, whether you want me there or not. I'll be next to you until there's no light. I can be taller then you, shorter, bigger or smaller. Sometimes you can't see me, but I can always see you. But when the sun is gone, I'll see you tomorrow when the sun rises again.

Jenny Yi   13

Jenny Yi, Age 13, Thornhill, ON
Royal Orchard Public School

If I were your shadow, I would go wherever you go. Jump with you and walk with you. I can't guide you, but I'll be with you until you die, whether you want me there or not. I'll be next to you until there's no light. I can be taller than you, shorter, bigger, or smaller. Sometimes you can't see me, but I can always see you. But when the sun is gone, I'll see you tomorrow when the sun rises again.